Winner of the Katherine Mansfield Short Story Competition 2004, Tracey Slaughter is a new writer who lives in Thames. She teaches English at university level.

Tracey Slaughter

National Library of New Zealand Cataloguing-in-Publication Data
Slaughter, Tracey.
Her body rises / Tracey Slaughter.
ISBN 1-86941-726-7
NZ828.309—dc 22

A VINTAGE BOOK
published by
Random House New Zealand
18 Poland Road, Glenfield, Auckland, New Zealand
www.randomhouse.co.nz

First published 2005

ISBN 1 86941 726 7

Design: Katy Yiakmis
Cover photo: Gettyimages
Cover design and other photographs: Christine Hansen
Literary agency services provided by Dr Susan Sayer
Printed in Australia by Griffin Press

Her body rises
stories & poems

TRACEY SLAUGHTER

v

Acknowledgement is made to the following journals, newspapers and anthologies where some of these poems and stories have previously appeared:

Poetry NZ, Landfall, New Zealand Listener, Waikato Times, JAAM, Bravado, Trout, Poetry Aotearoa, Takahe, Women's Studies Journal, Climbing the Flame Tree, Tapping the Tank, The Whole Wide World, An Exchange of Gifts, and *FIRE* (UK).

CONTENTS

I. WHEAT

I CUT MY SON'S HAIR & it falls like wheat.

That is what I'd remember.

The teacher in autobiography class says you choose what you remember, you make up your life like a story & select the details to set in your mind. When he says this I think: if this were true my mind would just be wheat now. My mind would be as clear as a window, but something with feelings . . . a bowl of skin . . . & through it there would only be the lightest drift of fibres. I'd see nothing, feel nothing but my baby's hair as he let me cut it . . . the first cuts dropping in stems of moisture, the lighter, drier pieces floating, glittering over the damp towel like grains. Like seeds.

But already there's a detail, there's the white towel below us. There's more than just wheat.

I'm a mother. We live in the details. I'm still a mother.

So I follow the detail back, to the piece of the day I can stand going into. We've just come from the shower & we spread his damp towel over the floor. We've trimmed his rustling head before & so we've left ourselves naked; we know when we finish we'll have to jump back in the shower. There'll be prickles & feathers caught in our mouths, in the folds of our throat, our elbows. Our belly button will be a cleft of dust & if we don't wash it out our skin will stay awake all night, wriggling.

I knot my towel over milky breasts & he sits in the shadow of my legs. His little warm white spine trickles down from his hair. We put the television on & let its pictures wash past us, but we turn down the sound so I'll sing to him instead. Sometimes he hums to the songs I make up against his ear, against his shoulder, little inside-out tunes that I murmur about his body, his name. We can stretch & rhyme whole operas out of his name, we play with it like a ribbon, winding it in & out through the alphabet, making a net of days. His name: the lonely vowels, the jump to open. I'm helping him know who he is . . . the sound of my mouth is the edge of his body. I'm hoping he'll remember this.

I'm hoping he'll remember this forever. Or at least one day . . . as he cleans his face when it belongs to a man, as he brushes a man's darker hair. Or perhaps as he shaves & the motes of his own hair drop from his body without him noticing.

Forever is never as long as you think it will be. It is only a clipping of wheat. It is a frond of light, & it falls. It falls.

Golden, I would write: golden. They don't let you write golden these days. Look, just look at the shape of it on the page, the teacher tells me: soft, overblown.

He writes it on the blackboard, golden. I want you to look at this word, he tells the class, I want you to study it. This word represents every cliché that I want you to cut from your language. This word is poeticism.

It is a demon in cherubic form. You must cast it out.

My son's hair was golden. Let me write golden. Let me write golden.

My other son, my oldest son, comes home from school with a note from his teacher. She is a trainee teacher, & the note is young & stupid & brief.

It says that my son has refused to take part in the school science topic of bees. *Bees* is highlighted for me, with a dark, a capital B. When my son is encouraged to participate he produces deliberate mistakes. Please find enclosed a sheet where I should observe the kind of sullen errors she means.

On the sheet there are fat cartoon bees, some looking like puffy cherubs, some looking like burglars with masks on their eyes & shady hats. Stamped in each of the cloudy bee bodies is a word that my son was supposed to use to fill in the gap in the sentences. Instead he has used one word repeatedly. The word is *eye*, & he's written it into most lines: *Bees work at building the eye, gathering nectar to make the eye & protecting the eye from robber bees. The Queen eye works the hardest. She doesn't eye until she dies.*

The only time he hasn't used the word eye is in the correct sentence: *She has a baby almost every time you blink your . . .* In this gap there's a whole list. WINGS, EGGS, ANTENNAE, EXOSKELETON, my son has written. He's cut the words into the page in jagged black strokes. He's written them in a spiky shell so the letters start to look like an insect.

She has a baby almost every time you blink your POLLEN, I read.

It was golden as we watched it darken & come off our skin in fringes of water. It was golden as I picked up the towel & shook it into a breeze from the kitchen door. It's golden as I get out of bed & go down into the living room & switch every light on & even get a torch & crouch where I cut his hair down on the floor. It's golden, golden in my mind, although I can't find a shred of it there, where I lost it. Not a seed, not a lash. Not a thorn.

I think of the policeman who had to take my son from me. I think now, as I thought then, this is the first time he's picked up a child.

You could see it in his body, you could see where the knowledge was missing . . . those signals in the collarbone, the wrists of people who know how to pick up a child. He spent a long time kneeling in front of us, just looking at us. The other people in the room must have thought he was moved, he was giving us time. Perhaps he was, yes he was, I think, but even more than that he was solving a problem. He was studying our bodies trying to look for places we might come apart. He was examining my son's legs, the neck that lay over my elbow, calculating the weight, the pressure, the words needed to break me from him.

It was a task, an assignment: to break us open where my bones held onto his bones, where my milk slipped over his ribs, where my hair & my breath & my fingernails kept asking his mouth to answer my singing.

To pick a child up out of that is no small act. What breaks milk, what breaks touch? He did it through pity.

He said, my sister's pregnant, & then his breath was very quick & hooked because he thought he'd said the wrong thing.

But almost at once I answered him. I said, don't tell her about this.

I remember silence. Then I remember looking at this man's shirt & saying, I don't want those buttons to scratch him. And he showed me how the silver buttons were on a ring which slid out through the pocket, & he held them down by the baby's scalp where my hand was fixed through all his hair.

Can you hold them for me? he asked.

That was all I could do for him. I couldn't move any further . . . just open my hand & let them fall in like stones.

We were a problem in gravity & he was the instrument that had to solve it. And I pitied him.

I take the note to my son's classroom. When I enter I can't breathe. The walls are hung with her life cycle, & down from the ceiling she floats from orange strings. She's not a cartoon now, her multiplied bodies are glossy & jointed & accurate. She flies through the seasons marked out around the room & I see her in Spring, squatting, strands of gleaming egg split from her abdomen, her fur, her veiny wings. I sit down on a desk: in Summer she hovers on nests of waxy cocoons. Inside each oval egg there's a pupa, its exoskeleton gathering on it like finger-nails.

The teacher finds me. I'm sick in the cylinders of nectar the children have sellotaped from cut-down bottles. I catch it all in the water they have thickened with glue & coloured yellow, & when I am finished I pass it to the teacher. I tell her why my son will not be taking part in the science project. She shakes a little but she gives me a list of other topics we might select.

I look down the list & I see wheat.

Butterflies, I tell her.

But every time you blink your eyes there is pollen. The last thing I see when I leave the room is the light that throbs on the dark husk of the queen.

The teacher of autobiography splits the word into three sections: autos, bios & graphe. He tells us again to consider how each of these is constructed, how even before we commit our autobiography to paper we have processed our life story through choices of perception, pressures of what may not be said. Decisions to forget.

I point out that in the middle there's something that we don't construct, not always.

He queries. The body, I say.

He says, we construct our physical life through language, language filters the body. We remember our body only in terms of what our language can say.

I start to say, no, sometimes it's the other way, the other way, but I can't explain it.

He says, the fact that you can't explain it is evidence for what I've explained.

But in the middle I see the sleeping thorax, the long clear wing. I see the atmosphere of my eye flushed with the grain of my son's drifting hair. I hear the pulse of my baby's throat as it pollutes itself, as it boosts its tissues . . . with what? . . . with water, with fear, with vessels of nothingness which close him away from me.

Into their blue nerves, into their dark blooming.

The teacher is right in one way . . . there's no vocabulary for this.

But outside of language the memory still comes. It comes to the body.

I don't *construct* my son's mouth as I hook it & call & drag it with mine. I don't *construct* the wires of milk that keep working down from my shoulder blade trying to cloud life through the nipple because his mouth is *there*, because the breast remembers. It knows the brush of light against his teeth.

This would not be part of my story. I would not remember this.

You wind & pin sheets around the milk but it still moves to the memory of him.

The body can't *decide* to forget.

I would not choose to remember him the way other parts of the dream sometimes make me. Sometimes in the dream I'm in the shower & I hear his voice asking if he can come in. Maybe, some nights, I slide the door open & take off his clothes as they soften with steam. I count his buttons, which he calls bubbles, or help him find words for the parts of his body which pull out of the blue cloth, ankles, ears, knees. I feel him moving around me in the spray as he plays with the toy he has smuggled, the branch of his hand on my leg for balance, the feather of his hair against my hip. When he stops & leans against me the current of his humming brings my bones to the surface.

Other times I just shuck his clothes roughly without talking of his body. I don't notice his body because I don't yet know that I will lose it.

Sometimes I just say no. I'm tired & I don't want to let him in. I hear his voice fill & gulp, but I concentrate on the sound of the water. I don't see the clear print of his hand banging, banging the flushed glass. I've raised my own hands up to the water & I'm staring at it tracing my empty palms.

I should go to church, the young man says. I might find something there I could turn to.

The autobiography teacher has put us in pairs, to discuss early memories of books. The boy I'm paired with says the Bible. Daniel, Jonah, the animals were what he loved.

I say, *Where The Wild Things Are*, the last book I ever read to my son.

The boy says, they thought there was something. They've wondered, the class. My grief is a rumour here.

He has a beautiful skinny face & his eyes are sexual. Along his arm the muscle of an older man grows in a plait. A vein rises, forks. When he says the word church, it comes out rich & lonely.

I tell him the Bible is just a book about dead children to me.

I go into my oldest son's room. I sit on his bed with him, & tell him he won't have to study bees. He opens a drawer & takes out fist-shaped papers. He's crushed them with precision, but I see edges of hives, a head draped in net.

There's a diagram which tells us of the hive wall, its algebra. I close this sheet in my bigger hand until we can't see any of its symmetry, its shine.

I say, what about butterflies?

Crabs, he says. He wants to do crabs.

When I ask him why, he says he remembers being at the beach with his brother. They were paddling in the creek which broke off the hard waves into the shade. I remember what he's going to say . . . that there was a white crab drifting in foam & he scooped it out, & the two boys opened its body slowly with a stick.

So he knew about crabs . . . because I told him, he says against my chest.

They listened to it creaking & they looped weed out of its claw. Then my oldest son took his brother into the shallows to show him the soft dark holes, the quick chisel of legs that sucked down into them.

We told him about them, I know we did, he says through my ribs. We warned him.

He gets out a page where he's started on crabs. He's drawn one with crusts & nails & bubbles. Under it he's written, *If they see a bigger animal they hide under a rock or in the sand.*

You know so much, I tell him, & he leans back on me & we sit there.

Death is a bigger animal, & so is grief.

It was the same towel. It was loose & warm when I pulled it off the wash line.

I hear the small hook of sound as it plucked on the steel.

Perhaps if I'd been the kind of mother who folds things neatly into the basket.

But I'm not.

I shake things out inside. He's always laughed when I've done this. He's always shrieked & pulled a face at the flocking noise of cloth in air. He's always laughed & grabbed at the hanging ripples of shirt, at the wagging nappies.

I watch the towel swell into the air between us. It holds for a moment, rigid, fragile . . . like a wing in the space between my knuckles and his.

The dark body splits from it like an atom.

The bee is lazy. It lets death out with a shrug.

The laugh is the last thing his throat knows. He points & laughs as the cloth sky comes down to wrap him.

The autobiography teacher tells me I must cut, I must edit.

He gives me a story to use as a model. This is death, he says. Death comes with no adjectives. Death is in the distance between the body & the verb.

I tell him the policeman came back with an envelope of hair. But it was dead hair. I don't want my writing to be like that hair, something cut from him after he's dead. I want to find a language that moves on the page like he did, & sometimes I do hear it . . . something in an adjective that moves like skin. Something in a line that shifts like his head at my breast or his heel on my ribcage.

He says, a monument's not a soft thing. Your language needs sealing, hardening.

He goes on, you can't bury a child in a tomb of metaphors.

I don't go back to class.

There are whole pages here for women like me. There are black prayers, Latin under plastic. There are leaves & curls set into a cross. My son helps me turn through the pages. He wants me to choose another picture, but he's satisfied when I tell him the reason for wheat.

We watch the woman. She is orderly with the steamed tools, the long clean needles. Cut into her shoulder is a fairy with a stick of stars. It's a woman's parlour . . . no flames, no skulls, just the inking of loved ones, of lost ones. I open my shirt & she washes from my collarbone down to the core of my breast.

Can he get a crab when he gets bigger? my son asks me.

Yes, I tell him, if he still wants to, he can get a tattoo when he gets big.

The site is clean. The woman asks my son if he can hold back my hair. She prepares to lower the needle, pauses before she embeds the first black stroke.

Am I sure I know what it will feel like?

I know what she will say. Like sunburn, she tells me . . . but at its deepest, it may feel like a bee-sting.

II. HER FIRST

THE DRESS HAD BONES. *NOT real ones*, Olive said to her daughter, Adrienne. Yet Olive had a memory of historical garments in her own mother's chest of drawers, ribbed with a wing-like pattern said to be achieved by thin internal bones. *It takes a man's backbone*, Olive's father used to say — a phrase soon attached to this hard undergarment in his daughter's head, the result of which was her childhood impression that women weren't fitted with quite enough bones, so an extra skeleton was sewn into their clothes. And it fitted so well to her mother's flesh, this miscomprehension of feminine buttressing — the looseness and softness she knew from accidental glimpses of her mother undressing, or felt pressed absorptively around her face in midnight callouts from nightmare, as opposed to the uniform, unmoving figure that appeared beneath her mother's housecoat in the day. Her mother simply rose from the bed with the warm unsupported beauty of her body — which was in itself a fluid, alluring dress of silvery but impractical skin — and over it she laced on the off-white exoskeleton.

When Adrienne stands at the hall door the dress is somehow standing out around her. The bracing, which she told her mother she didn't *want* anyway, seems to be keeping her ball gown half a centimetre away from her skin. It has been an unnerving experience, to go bra-less for the evening, and the sense that wind is whispering between dress and skin is not soothing. Two of the bones run vertically up the bodice in line with her nipples — she can feel the dress's pressure just touching the tip of each. They respond, moving forward as if opening tiny invisible mouths.

The theme this year is Polynesian. Uprooted palm trees are propped up with rocks in the centre of the dance floor. Clouds of dry ice drift out at intervals from this unstable oasis and several couples are already waltzing badly around in the mist. The serving staff, shining white children selected from the younger school, are dressed in sarongs with hibiscus taped to their wrists and neck, and in their hair. Bikini-topped, some of the waiting-girls are hoping to win over an older boy — a finger under the strap perhaps, or a mouthful of skin in the kitchen during a dark, slow song. Needing a strong hand to halve the hairy, difficult globes of the coconuts has provided the perfect excuse to call them in.

'Whalebones, I believe,' says Olive. She is fitting the dress on Adrienne, inside out. The raw seams, still with their broken lines of thick red tacking, look like markings for surgery. A last-minute arterial map. Some of the pieces still have their transparent paper attached. Adrienne has always loved the tender unfolding of a dress in stages. The laying out of the pattern, her mother poring over it silently, searching out the tiny hieroglyphics on inside facings, sleeves and backs.

'Whalebones, that'd be right,' says her brother. 'Only a whale would make'm in her size.'

This is a remark which Olive cannot let pass.

'That will be enough out of you,' she says. But she still has her lips pressed down upon a line of pins, and the reprieve sounds softly out of one side of her mouth.

Adrienne has never liked to see her mother with pins in her mouth. As a child she would stand terrifyingly still for her fittings, never moving her eyes from that cold line-up of heads in her mother's mouth — she would even count them, to assure herself that Olive never accidentally let one slip, its shiny sting behind the pink compression of her lips. A taste like paper-clips, old thin metal, puncturing the wet wall of her cheek, the valve of her throat as she swallows. Once Adrienne even

HER BODY RISES

brought home from Brownies a pin-cushion in the shape of a sun-hat, with a ribbon to wrap it around her mother's wrist. It is her favourite thing to play with, when Olive lets her explore her sewing table. Adrienne ties it to herself and discovers, if she watches very closely, she can see her pulse quivering the tin stalks of the pins.

'How'd they get the whalebones then? Did they kill whole whales just for ladies' dresses?'

Olive gathers the last finger-breadth of silk against her daughter's body, smoothly inserts the last pin. 'No, whales were used for lots of things,' although she cannot think of a single one.

'Oil,' shouts Adrienne's brother from his homework, 'they melted them down in pots. And lipstick.'

'I'm sure they didn't have lipstick in the nineteenth century, thank you, William.'

Adrienne, never good at history, is left with an image of a whole whale skeleton, hollowed out from the inside and towed in over the ocean. Left to dry like a fine white house in the salt air, an old museum exhibit on the sand. Far out at sea, its slippery flesh will be floating, or sinking, like bolts of material jettisoned from a ship in distress. Lying loosely on or under the water in oily frills.

Adrienne hasn't actually gone to the ball with a partner. She has gone along with her best friend Meri and her boyfriend. This would normally be an occasion for shame — but it is acceptable to school opinion because everybody knows there *is* a boy who *wanted* to go with Adrienne. Adrienne is a victim of premature invitation. Phillip, thinking Adrienne wouldn't want to go with him, asked another girl just as a friend — a category, like *consolation prize*, which is attached to many of the night's couples. It has all been straightened out in advance, and it is now understood, even by Phillip's partner (who is herself hoping to end up with someone else), that Adrienne and

Phillip, after a decent interval, will end up together for the evening. A more private pre-dance arrangement involves Meri and Scott, Phillip and Adrienne ending up in a combi van borrowed from Phillip's Dad.

The last school dance was a P party, and everyone had to go dressed as something that started with the letter P. Meri and Adrienne decided to go as the Phantom of the Opera and his Prima Donna. Meri's dark hair was slicked back until it felt like stone on her head, and she wore a man's suit and hat. She had the underworld charm of the mafia. Adrienne found an old wedding gown in a local op-shop, with a breathless white bodice that hoisted up her small breasts, and yellow crusts like a halo of sweat from the underarms. They couldn't find a veil and so they hung thick trails of lace from Adrienne's hair. The dance committee had hired one of those lights that electrified everything white, making everyone into their own negative. Adrienne's dress went the colour of toothpaste, and she streaked the air like a ghostly vapour caught on film.

Meri and Adrienne had made the phantom's mask in the bathroom the weekend earlier. Meri's hair had looked like oil as she lay on the white tiles of the floor. Adrienne put a pink and white drinking straw into Meri's mouth, and then began to cover her face with layers of papier-mâché. Slowly the white pulp began to take on the shape of nose and cheek-bones. The sodden hollows of Meri's eyes lay back in her head, taking longer to form. In and out of the thin straw whistled the sound of Meri's breathing.

Adrienne slid her fingers in the thick mixture of her friend's face. The wet bulk was becoming heavy and the sloppier mass in the middle was not drying as fast as the forehead or chin. 'Don't move,' Adrienne said, 'you can't move, it's not dry yet.' But a low panic was humming up from the tiny vent of Meri's mouth, and suddenly she got up and scratched the mask from her head.

Adrienne had taken infinite care in packing the face out with paper and tissue, leaving it under the fluorescent light in Meri's bathroom to set.

They pull the van as close to the beach as they can get it and kiss vigorously. The sounds from their throats are not as loud as the groanings of the old van. But eventually Meri and Adrienne have to get out to go to the toilet — they had meant to go before leaving the hall but when they got to the cloakroom they found a gleaming reservoir of vomit in the cubicles and filling the tin troughs along the wall.

They pick their way down through the crispy tide-line of seaweed, blacker than darkness. They feel other left-overs under their feet — a wet plastic bag, fishing line, a jandal. Some summers, jellyfish have been a problem here, the beaches opened and closed according to their swarms. At a distance their bodies along the shore are like clots of colour-less icing — coming close, they are loose bags of clearness, coloured lace-like veins afloat inside.

Kissing and rustling have pushed the bones of Adrienne's dress up through her bodice. As she moves she feels a slight scratch on her chest, like a fingernail. Her face muscles hurt. With both hands she touches the thick hinge of bone just in front of her ears — it opens, aching smoothly. Her lipstick has worked to a hard paste around the edges of her lips. The heavy smell of the sea rolls over the beach.

When they reach the firmer sand, they squat close together, pulling up their dresses. Their urine sounds like lemonade, hisses back at the thin expression of the sea. The warmth of their piss seems to shine back under their bodies from the cold sand. They stay squatting down for a moment, letting the sea's breath dry them off.

'Me and Phillip. Do you want us to — you know, go for a walk or something?' She has heard their urgency rubbing the vinyl of the van's long front seat. Limbs repositioned and the dials of the dashboard struck.

'No. No, God no. Don't go anywhere. Promise you won't.'

Their dresses inhale, exhale. The sea is very close to sliding under them. Almost full, the moon lets light run down into the water. Moon-edged too, their faces. The sea makes the sound of itself, listening. Their bodies almost brush the sand. They are silent — and each thinks this is the most beautiful moment of the evening. The closest they have come to the night itself.

Getting up, Adrienne lets down her dress and prises back up her pantyhose. Around her waist they leave a saggy line of unrolled skin. 'I hate these things,' she says. 'But they have their uses. They sure stop fingers.' And suddenly she thinks that Phillip deserves this disappointment. She wonders what she feels like to him, the softened top of her thigh, her hip, pressed down under the damp net of the tights.

At this same beach Adrienne and her brother have gone piping. They stand looking down in the slack shape of the harbour mouth, letting the sea suck their feet back in time. Mud laps their feet down, moves into the soft crotches between their toes. They bend down into the hollows and feel for the rough teeth of the pipis, clattering them into the plastic bucket.

'What did the blind man say when he passed the fish shop?' William shouts against the out-tide's wind. She shakes her head, thinking of nothing that can answer him, but seeing anyway the wavy pink flesh of the fish pulled out of its sequinned skin.

'Hi, girls,' shouts William. 'Get it, got it? Morning, girls.'

Adrienne has no idea.

'That's what they say it smells like,' he says. 'Like fish.' He waves a crusted shell at her grinning. 'A fish finger,' he splutters in triumph, stroking at the tuft of wet green hair. 'Mmm, seafood,' he teases. No response. 'Fish, fish,' he shrieks. He starts to prance in the sand. His feet make sloppy holes, soon washed in.

HER BODY RISES

After a while he gives up and goes back to digging up the shellfish. At home later, Adrienne cracks one open, puts her face close into the shell. She looks at it, the dangling valve, the thickly finished selvedge. Its skin is clammy, pale like the membrane that forms at the neck of the milk bottle. She thinks that it smells nothing like the delicate gust that rises from her in the toilet stalls, the collective smell that the girls carry out to the incinerator, wrapped in their hands.

Adrienne and Meri cut the mask into shape later. They borrow a pair of garden secateurs off Meri's mother.

'Perhaps if we'd just made it half to start with.'

'No, we couldn't have done it that way. It wouldn't have held its shape.'

Adrienne curves out at the chin, in around the mouth space, back up over the nose to cover the rest of the face. She punches in eye holes, smooths the rough edges with a nail file. Then she paints it a perfect white, through which the eye holes look back in perfect darkness. Adrienne thinks the mask looks like a beautiful halving of Meri — like Meri with a wave broken over her face.

Adrienne does Meri's make-up, layers of white over her dark skin. To finish she uses crimson lipstick to paint on a huge, misshapen mouth. With black eyeliner Adrienne puts in a small broken line like a row of stitches. Meri's mouth looks swollen, tugged sideways. 'One must suffer to be beautiful, that's what my mother says.'

Meri and Adrienne win the award for best costume. They mount the spot-lit steps to the stage, Adrienne carefully holding up her train.

Of course, not real bones, she reinforces to her daughter, years later. She is threading the flat, synthetic derivative into the invisible channels of her daughter's gown. But perhaps, she thinks, real bones would be better. The plastic fibres of these alternatives constantly threaten to snag the tender interior of the dress. She has to work very slowly, edgily; she achieves no glide, she thinks, no rhythm. She remembers herself running down onto her first beach in this country — she had on something light, it flows behind her, even without the wind. There had been signs there, historical details of how the beach had belonged to the whalers. High on a dune, a white picket railing encloses, she cannot quite remember, the first girl born here or a sailor's grave. She thinks there may have been old cauldrons, pots rusted out and lying on their sides on the beach — they are caves for the children, who make echoes of themselves inside, and also burn their feet. Not far from the beach was a shop where she bought a little black plastic baby doll, with green tattoos on her puffy cheeks and a skirt made of cut plastic tubes threaded over clear line. The boards of information looked down from the car park and the council rubbish bins, saying things about the whalers, the many deaths ashore and at sea. Olive had taken little notice, simply so happy to be arrived. In the memory, though, Olive thinks there may have been vertebrae, large hard shapes like a ship's cleats and anchors, waiting to tie distant vessels to the sand.

The thin silk catches. So vulnerable it is suddenly repellent. Some moments it seems her fingers have a desire for the smooth, clean movements she imagines belonging to bone.

The dress does not look like it was made for her. It looks like a negative of someone else, a long white mould, something formed by winding plaster and bandages around another woman's body. It could crack like a shell at any moment, making the thick wet sound of a mollusc opening, and she will slide out, succulent, unsurprised.

III. A SMALL RED PARABLE

At twenty-seven she learns her ladders and the baby falls.

Two years back she moves in a white house where the windows have broken sashes.

At two she developed a way of losing her breath but winning arguments.

A piece of concrete holds the clues, a handprint, pressure vein, gum, dandelion.

The baby fed for three months badly, thin milk splitting her nipple.

The x-ray of her left wrist shows it was broken but won't say how.

Custody arrangements have been made for the benefit of everyone.

Some time later destiny took love from her like a piece of skin. At sixteen, of course, a religious experience.

Ten years is the maximum for holding your mother's hand, after that you must cross roads without your fingers signalling emptiness.

Twenty-one is a day to throw out clothes, blue make-up and lockable diaries, where people stand for capital letters.

The lost breath holds itself together in a hidden sac of her body.

A diligent and friendly student, but hampered by frequent illnesses, nevertheless a virtuoso Lady Macbeth.

You notice looking at your child that the eye is constructed of tiny fibres.

Men like nineteen heavily painted, wet with the sound of yes.

At six the sunshine tells a long fairy-tale, kisses push up under her skin.

The lost breath practises poetry trying to find the sounds it should have made.

One day at the races she remembers an injured horse.

She turns up once in a dress her mother made and her stepmother takes her home.

And the stall floor clotting hotly with its arterial pumpings.

Mummy's here, go back to sleep.

At seven she spends a whole afternoon in her grandfather's garden, swatting with a tennis racket at white butterflies.

At nine the solicitor arrived to allocate matrimonial property, her mother made soft noises and smashed dishes in the sink.

At dinner time you must eat what you're given.

Seventeen butterflies in the strings.

She takes voices out of her depth and bites the side of her fingers, paste is applied to her hands but the bad sounds travel around her head.

At two the baby takes a three dollar map of the earth to bed.

*

in the morning they redden their mouths
to make the shape of a heart cut out

or a warm seal on a letter
sent to anyone in love forever

*

Did you love me? You were hard to
resist. In lessons I wrote your name all over
my books & pencil case as if
the alphabet was something you owned.

Slow & thick, in white-out I remember
the smell of my absorption painting
down your name's hard bones.

Sometimes if you sat with me in class
you touched it up — I watched you, rubbing the crust
upon a syllable, peeling off the thin film
of a letter with your thumb.

You liked to write
your name & that you *were*
here. Past tense.

*

the sky is full of things
you've forgotten — like butterflies
that fix the stars in your ears. Holes
like this in your body were things you
cried for as a child. Almost grown &

angry you went to the back room
& chose two beautiful blooms
of glass that looked like
bacteria under a slide. They
put a gun to your head & you went
home to repaint the hair
around your eyes.

*

my lover, ghosts
are nothing — compared to
what bodies can do.

*

She likes the city
because she dreams
of dying there.

It has few sins
that don't show
like skin stretched over light.

*

In the headmistress's garden
you'll find the best hopscotch stones.
They are riverbed grey and uniform.
They'll jump if you ask them.

Under your hand you feel
the sound as they slide to their chalked-in numbers.

*

I should have taken
risks, walked through red
lights. Streets like

veins which meet in
darkness having found
no exit from
the heart.

*

she lies inside
a square of light

her body rises
to the occasion

*

Nothing on your mind
without the fingerprints
of memory. Your eyes
are dark as islands you
interpret with the shadows
of your past. The hollowness
of all this is the fault of
one day on the water
where you took your clothes
off & believed you had
swallowed him whole. Love
sinks with your skin through
several tides of hardly knowing
him. A few hot grains of sand
were at the corner of his
mouth. Let this syllable mark
the distance between our
bodies & the light that left
them under itself like silence —
the heart's weed pressed at
the water's edge.

*

She has imagined belonging
to a body — where would it
end, in the bed, in
yesterdays?

You could place it only
by light shining from
its fingernails — memories at
the edge of its teeth, its red
dress in fiction.

It ends with this
exposure — the big teeth

are black, the light from
the open mouth.

*

slow-limbed under
the oak shade you see
schoolgirls lying on
their bellies, practising
their autographs
at playtime.

*

You ate me like fruit
& left the core out.

The heart is resilient in its sin.

It breathes in & out on the myth of itself.

Touch him, & the skin goes slack & full
with the rhythm of the guiltless.

It is a black plum, preserved in voices.

It won't be paraphrased; it will love
him to death.

Listen to the damp sound of it flowering:
apocalypse, apocalypse.

It has eaten your pleasures; it will always
talk with its mouth full.

The heart lets down its red
scarf, draws him on.

the laundress

*

you expect a history of limbs
a wash house hung with breathing

*

that music box was always mirror-pink
that plastic bitch was dancing
venom in her letters, fire in your wings

*

generous relations
a hissing bloom of skin

*

take your pick
a cradle cracked, a mouth
of branches
shrill signs on her

*

come into my parlour
there is cake & semen
dead flies on the sill

*

she had a gentle garden
it was full of sticks & stones

*

always on the night
her name was Mary
Mary, quite

HER BODY RISES

*

there were residents who hit the bottle
ghosts welled up like saucepans
boiling hearts of meat & string

*

you like to think of fingerprints
an aureole & she'll
forgive you, giving being yellow in
the water like her gown

*

a flask of silk
a clock face made of flowers

*

hips like seashells
chambers howl

*

tide sucks on your finger
salted creature in a hole
a curl of rotten dreaming

*

send in the clowns she sang
its tin teeth glitter

*

a foaming blend of darkness
suddenly falling dead at a tub

*

something comes from the vulnerable trees
your belief in moonlight

his anticipation
tongue, rain

*

the family is not dark
but watch their faces lit
by yellow mirrors

*

generally, love peels back
isn't it rich, your skirt of hearts is broken

*

your filmy goodbye
a yolk of metal stars
your snot on his mouth

*

haven't you listened, flakes of water
spray of bones through fallen clothes

my heart has recorded your absence. It
is attenuated — rootless, slender

it makes its obedient sounds. You're
a space in a room where blood won't gather

& where muscle & shadow won't pull each
other into the shape of love.

endlessly over what happened to us
it has learned not to go on repeating

itself. It still has many questions but
it doesn't stop to hear your answers.

something must be done about the moon

The moon alone is capable of murder.

The moon will piss on her place in fairy tales if she's drunk enough.

They tied her hands behind her back but she didn't sign the confession.

She makes long phone calls like a teenager who won't hang up first.

The moon has poisoned the water but made a dream of ribbons you can sleep in.

She's sure to be harbouring soviets in her svelte fur.

The moon is a pattern of malice & indecision.

She had children but kept them in her belly & made them eat blood.

The moon is present in many romances.

She wrote a song but they hollowed it out for a boat & pushed it into the river.

The moon is an old stenographer & she takes down details thin & fast.

They held an engagement on her decks & the face of the young couple shone like pots & pans after generous scouring.

The moon is apparently purple & undisturbed.

During the day the moon lives under the bridge which halves the town for lovers who need to live in two to be in love.

The moon is a bulge of heartlessness; if you licked her she'd taste like silver.

The moon drove over the edge by the beach where young girls back down in station wagons.

HER BODY RISES

You're so heavy under the eyes; the moon keeps her groceries there, & a bag packed for hospital in case you fall & miss her red carpet.

The moon is a spider vein burst in the sky; they can remove her with laser treatment.

She left a fingernail out to trip up the prince.

The moon got married too young & learnt the hard way; welcome to the real world the moon's mother said.

She took the quiz in a magazine & scored what you'd expect of a cipher.

The moon is an autobiographer but she works in pencil to avoid prosecution.

The moon has been used enough, leave her alone.

The moon would zip up her skirt & hitch to a town where you don't hear their voices.

Hey diddle diddle the moon walked into a door; that's the official version.

She chews up the dead so you can digest them.

*

little red lone wolf
lives in the thorax of the shopping mall
a destiny of buckles & flowers
will not teach her to
clean up her smile

soon you'll say her
paraphrase of blood

I'm a big fan
of flames

*

pat-a-cake
make me a bouquet
of carsick

I'm a sticky rebel now
come see my face
of baby seed

just outside the lexicon of trees
we're in their supple darkness
I wanted to make this elemental
gristle us with stars

*

he takes her to a dark flat
they go wild with patrimony

                                        the bed clouds with her
                                            epileptic jazz

they shake down
angels from the ceiling

*

walk in & spread
my skirt of chains

                                                watch it go up
                                            the sky's integument

I've led you round
by a cigarette
so I can see your lower half in ash

*

a song, a bad long list of sores
& treasure, *I am not a rose*

                                                they take us for
                                        a school trip into rumours
                                            where the treaties float

on yellow bones of petticoat
a weathered dress of wire, he said
the fabric of the feminine is broken

*

cut the film
the red queen is the lead
of faces in your hand

                                    the tissue with
                          its cells of ink: the shallow
                  print the lighter tones, the deepest
                              hold the darkness

the dialect of clouds
we drink their ammunition

*

slip with me
we'll test a sea of stolen parts

                  light the dump with holden headlights
                          & the rifle flowers. Gulls
                      applaud with dislocated wings

litus, litoris, the shore

*

be warned, the eye can
still a moment, watch
that day's venation for a lifetime

                                    yes, your causal mouth

what must be done
involves a bed

*

the red jack
such a helpless
porn star

how can these be
organs of flight?

by letterbox her mother
says, the flowers are inside
in deep water
this is my parenthesis of shadows

*

a backpack of tissue samples
a diary of holy salt

I'm in origami bruises
I'm in bone-buttoned skin

low joule, blown the school
flash you my
silver-backed smile

*

I've got a vein-blue gram
of *freak out*
that uproots capillaries of wanting

you tell me, when she crossed
a memory, she took
a cutlass

sub, under, *cutis*, skin
back then, you'd think it was pentecostal

*

you were so good at getting
that look in your eye, a blue kite

lone wolf goes to her reunion   53

of suicide notes, an archive of fingerprints
that push too far

> how the static flowered on
> your scalp & this was politics
> the dark groin's beehive
> junkmail & my humming box

we only missed
by the water's calculus

*

in the phraseology of moon
I see your body quote itself

> your clavicle gives love a shirt of light
> a wing of clouded oil

so high school
lit itself up with its own
addiction

*

line up my tongue
the methylated red crack
of my melancholy, *sooooooooooo sorry*

> cheer for your blonde gorgon
> voodoo-doll head-girl

forgive us
our metrical darkness
our muscled cries

*

I've led you round

HER BODY RISES

by an outgrown mouth
its dermis & its conscience

                                    a girl can't help
                            her palmistry, the dumb boy's
                                honey-fondled stalking

hanker for my corpse of media cuttings
with your jacked-off mind

*

the bed of entropy
you've dreamt of
fire fights itself against her dress

                            I've had my little red fill
                                    of *crackling song*

you make a good joseph
pull back the curtain
I'm up to my guts in god's light

*

everything you
did that day was fiction.

*

If you had taken
a map with you,
you'd watch

your fingers open it

the creased sea closed
on signs that show the cold
ways into town.

But you turned into shadows,
left the edge
where red runs down
the land & leaves

it hanging, long past
places where your skin
can count back to the sea.

*

egz-hast', *v.t.*
[*L. exhaurio, exhaustum* — *ex*, out, up
and *haurio*, I draw, draw water.]

To draw out or drain off the whole of;
to consume or use up;

to leave nothing unsaid regarding.

*

I could've met you

at that corner
in the furred bones of a tree
like we were children.

Then you always
had less fear than me.

Where the ends were wire
like blood twigs fraying in a lung
you climbed them.

You didn't call out to me.

The cold air
bloomed, your body
roared with it.

*

There's no guilt,
the chaplain says

but my son finds its shape
as children do.

Can you still see someone
if your eyes are closed? he asks me.

*

step-brother, step, *step*
we used to dance
while in the other

room our parents
traded partners

or play *murder*
in the dark

one child left
to be the body

face down in the hallway
trying not to pee

*

you handled it
with blood at first

then lost your nerve
with the incision.

It took you years
to finish.

*

I didn't come to
see your body.
I had two boys &
couldn't put them down.

> a box: wood, red
> (like their book) with a hook

They'd seen you
three weeks earlier,
one still feeding
one asking for cappuccino
in a four-year-old way.

They thought you were
a film star or a giant.

> oh! look at this mess
> the mother gets left: my son
> tipped-hat, tongue-thick, reading himself

We were both lullabied out.
We'd both been on the graveyard
shift with babies, laughed
at my black eyes & your grey hair.
You or me, one of us, said
aren't we blessed?

I don't tell them
how you're dead.

Boys, they say, are better at it.

with a bump — they don't
come back

*

that afternoon you saw the yellow spines
of hills, the weight of your son's hair

still on your shirt

*

& where you stopped the water
ran down onto someone else's wife, another skin

of grey clothes under trees that sort the sky-parts
into shades of light & smoke-prints from her mouth.

You knew that she'd have children
& that children kept her from the sea.

But you'd left notes, & bottles
for the house you'd broken in.
You closed your eyes:
a street of burns was ready like a birth-mark.

*

but to do it
breathing —

perhaps you
liked the irony.

Letting your soft cage
those drifting trees of blood

make slow fools of themselves.

*

step brother, *half*-step

the *chicken dance*
we did, *night fever*

You put your whole self out.

wives walking

*

along that road
the dead were given

too many plastic
flowers. We

both had inside
mothers, the kitchen

kind, who stood as if
listening for

something. A
stray net, the

sibilance
of shopping lists

*

we kicked along
gravel like

black seeds, me
in my cut

down dress, you with
nothing tucked in,

muttered about their
dogsbody hearts

HER BODY RISES

*
I carried
a drink & a curfew

but we stopped to
write our initials on water.

Your shirt was
wet & the wrong things

we had yet
to do made sense

*
one ripe angel
couldn't smell our

bodies going on
beneath her, but we never

stepped on
the kid in the chalky

arms of Jesus
deeper into

that block. The one
with the wind toy

a wood-cutter
wearing a folk suit

whose little axe went
click, click, click.

The only thing
in town to do was to

imagine dying
young

*
back on
the green wood wharf

I said, they grow
dead wives here. *True,*

I know the night planks
when they slip up

to walk one
last kiss. You could

gulp then,
grin as we knelt

to look for
the flex of weed, the

threads &
hammers of her
inner ear

*
your knuckle fit
in place of the angel's

nose, your
thumb stuck out her

tongue. You gave
her a mum's

voice: don't talk
to me like that young

man, you're getting
too big for

your box

*
I bit you
once, you twitched

against that little
stone hotel. There was

a beetle big as
an ashtray

a stick-shape
of plane above your

mouth in the
sky. Don't ask me

back: my shadow has
gone to ground

IV. SLEEPING OVER

THE FIRST TIME I EVER caught sight of a naked man it wasn't my father. My Dad left for work in a suit sometimes before we even got up, and came home in the same suit when we were mostly sleeping. If we weren't quite asleep we'd see the shadow of that suit shuffle down the hallway, and sometimes an arm of it came round the door, along with the gritty breathing of my father. I liked the kind of sigh he'd give — me and my sister were fairly cute, we knew, when we'd let our pink cheeks and mouths go loose pretending to be asleep. We'd even helped each other with our poses for it. 'Let's go dead to the world,' my sister would say, and we'd rush to our beds, coaching each other on how to make our hair splash out, throw our hands above our heads or leave wrists dangling over the mattress (always palm up, fingers curled, so we could see the nail polish). Something about the idea of a prince creeping up on you, finding you 'deep in slumber' (that was how my sister said it) really got our little hearts gulping. My sister could even make little sweet groans go in and out with her breath, but I'd get the giggles trying that trick. We particularly liked pulling swoons on long car drives, letting our bodies slip from side to side on the sticky vinyl, often pinching one another if someone was floating too far over the seat. Sometimes we'd still be dead to the world when Dad pulled into the driveway: whichever one of us got picked up by Dad always flopped extra blissfully.

But some nights Dad's sigh over our bodies wasn't a prince-like sigh at all. It was a tired sigh, like the one he gave when he pulled open his neck-tie, the only piece of clothing I ever saw him take off most work days. So, the first time I was likely to catch sight of a whole naked man, I guess it wasn't ever going to be Dad. And you could guarantee that Mum, who'd just about choked when my sister called me a 'cocktease' and I'd asked Mum to define it, wasn't going to be slipping us any clues about what jostled around inside a man's suit.

The night I got that first big look I was staying at a friend's place. We often played at each other's houses, and begged our Mums for the huge thrill of having a friend sleep over for the night. Then usually we'd wind up fighting, and someone would have to ring their Mother and get strapped sobbing into the car and be driven home again. We'd fight over who got to be the blonde girl from Abba, over who got to wear the wings in my dress-up box, over whose doll got to go on a date with Action Man and then have the little plastic baby swish out from under her silver disco skirt. Mostly we'd just hiss sulky things at each other, but sometimes biting did occur, and one time a jet of Charlie perfume got shot into someone's eyes. The weirdest thing that would happen though, when we got deep in an argument, was that my friend would start to swallow stuff. She'd get this heat rash run from her neck to her face like someone pulled up a pink net, and then she'd grab whatever she could, and shove it into her mouth and swallow it. Play-money, stick-on nails and make-up brushes, beads, they all went down. The little plastic baby went that way too. The hat and the dog from monopoly were never found. Then she would be off school the next day waiting to poo out these little trinkets, her mother making her do it on the potty so she could comb it through.

Why in the world a girl would do something like that I never thought to ask her. I simply got used to the look in her eye, and would scramble for somebody's mother if I thought she was going to start knocking things back. Both our mothers got pretty good too, at cutting us off before we got pissy, packing one of us, proud or mewling, back into the car. But the night that I got an eyeful of her father, there was no going home. My Mum and Dad had left town for a conference, my sister was off on her school camp. So I was sleeping over at my friend's place, and I was stuck there, whether we tried to yank out each other's guts with our fake nursing kits or not.

My friend's mother had taken the precaution of stripping my friend's room of all small things. This really disappointed me: my friend had the best collection of Barbie doll shoes (even ice-skates) I'd ever seen. But the teeny pink rubber stilettos were gone, as were the blue-bird-of-paradise earrings, the ladybirds off her hair-ties, the plastic peas from the Little Maid kitchenette. We echoed around in her bedroom for that first hour and everything we went to play with had something missing from its insides or some little bauble picked off its face, so the gaps started to spook me. I don't really know how to explain it, but what wasn't there kind of made me prickle, made my skin feel a little bit wet and sick. We started to play dress-ups, but even the buttons were gone from the bolero-jackets, the sequins gone from the shiny poncho and the chicken hat. So in the end we went into the living-room and watched an Elvis movie — he'd died not so long ago, so he was all over the TV.

The movie we were watching had the Elvis with moist hair and glossy cheeks, not the one that looked furry and sweaty in the big white jumpsuit. We got up and did the hula with him, pretending that we had head-bands and hip-hoops of flowers. When my friend's father came in he made us die of giggles from doing it with us, rolling down his overalls and jerking and flapping the arms around. He looked like Elvis, too, her father. He had the fuzzy sideburns and dark curls. But even if he hadn't looked like the King, he still would have been our hero. He was that mix of teasing fun and yes-sir authority all kids look up to. All the kids in the neighbourhood knew him too, and told tales about wacky things he did, like crashing the scooter into the rubbish pile or yahooing on the flying fox. He was the kind of Dad who built stuff, and tickled and brushed your hair at night, the kind of Dad who got on all fours and gave you bucking pony rides, who told stupid riddles and poured extra goo on your ice-cream when no one was watching, or when everyone was pretending not to see.

So we had a good night, I guess, and just about wet ourselves cackling with laughter before we finally got sent off to sleep. I would have been happy to hop straight into bed because I was feeling dozy, so I never knew what made my friend go weird while we were cleaning our teeth. We were standing in the bathroom and she suddenly grabbed for the blue glass goblet her mother had full of squishy bath oil gems. Right in front of my eyes she got a handful and started popping them like metal-coloured grapes into her mouth. By the time I shot down the hallway yelling she'd eaten nearly the whole stack of them, and a sticky yellow tentacle ran down her chin onto her nightdress.

It took me a long time to get off to sleep in her brother's bedroom. I wasn't used to it. Her brother was away on the same school camp as my sister, and his room smelt sour with real boy-fog. It ponged like a buried school lunch-box blooming with yuk under your bed, that smell of muzzled bread and snotty fruit pits. His sheets had been slept in too, you could feel the little balls of greying skin, the kind that rub off your toes and ankles if you hang out too long in the bath. I understood, in the scramble to sort out my friend, that the adults didn't have time to tuck me into a fresh bed, pat my head or read me a comforting story. But still, the night had taken the kind of twist that keeps a little girl thinking. So I practised my Snow White trance for a while, even mimed waking-up in the glass coffin, daintily spluttering out the chunk of poison apple in my throat. Gazing up at my prince, looking not at all peaky or decomposed. Somewhere in the story a real sleep must have got me.

But somewhere before real morning I thought I heard the sound of choking. Thinking about my friend bringing up the bubbles of oil nearly made me want to puke too. It was not like the kind of normal-night sound that goes on and on until you get used to it, so you know it's just your Dad bringing in the barbecue cover or the fig tree slapping the garage in a gale. Even at my friend's house I knew the sound the deckchairs made as they pumped in and out by the poolside, I knew the scuffle the cats made when they got into brawls in the yard. But that gagging was the kind of noise you know from the word go you're never going to sleep through, and the only thing to do is to get out of bed and track it down.

On the back of the brother's door was a fuzzy-felt dart-board with velcro fins poking out. Of course in light-time I'd seen it was there, but now I was in the almost-dark. The red and black net only started to take shape just as I walked smack into it. Bull's-eye, and how. I thought it was going to rock off the door, and I'd wake the whole house up. I kind of froze, staring into that dark web. When it stopped swinging from side to side, I got a hold of the door handle, and started to bluff myself with a bit of tough-talk: so what, if they hear you get up, maybe you need a squirt, or a drink of water? Even so I felt that every cell of my gut was listening for something. As I pressed open the door I felt exactly which muscles shifted in my hand.

It wasn't much more than a swish of hair, a flutter of eyes I pushed out into that hallway. Once I had seen what was coming towards me I swooped back into the room so fast I had that sensation of swimming past the edge of yourself that you get from a dream. The kind where you bounce right through your body, then lasso back up into your skin. But even when you get back into your bones it takes you a while to be sure of your brink — there's a fringe of shivers that make you feel superimposed on your flesh. So I jolted back and stood there for a few seconds and it was like trying to cut myself out of the dark.

When I heard the pulse of his footsteps, that snapped me out of it. I made another leap, this time a rush to the bed where

I jumped in and hooked the quilt right up over my face. If my sister had seen me she would have had to give me the prize for sure: with every nerve-ending I played up my princessy death, my rag-doll sloppiness. But for the very first time, I wanted to leave all the pretty out. For the first time in my life I'd seen every groove and weight of a man's big body, and it didn't make me feel like waiting around at all.

Whether he came into the room, like I thought I heard, I guess I won't ever know. I'd washed myself down so far into sleep my eyeballs felt like stones. He wasn't wearing a stitch, so it would seem a pretty strange thing for a father to do, to go into the room of a child sleeping over and stand there looking. Maybe he wanted to check I was okay. Maybe he never came in. It's just that I thought I heard the pluck of carpet as the door pushed open, the target bumping softly, the velcro's pop. It made me think twice about the cute faints we pulled like we were hexed little heroines: if you were knocked out for real you couldn't be sure that who was creeping up was the prince.

I didn't tell my sister my new thoughts about going dead to the world. By the time she got back from her camp, Mum had already sat me down at the kitchen table and told me there wasn't a conference after all. She and Dad had gone away to see if they could put their marriage together. 'It was a nice motel suite,' Mum said, and she had saved me the sewing kit, but what had been decided was that Dad would not be coming home. My friend's father had dropped me back, but instead of pulling out of our driveway he'd pulled a chair up beside my mother and while she was speaking I watched his hand on her knee. It wormed around till she got goosebumps. On the hard tips of his fingers a web of cracks was filled with diesel. His Elvis sideburns bristled as he rubbed his grin across my cheek.

He stayed for that whole week, and didn't go home until another swallowing incident called him back to my friend's house in the middle of one night. But this time it wasn't my friend who had been trying to digest doll's accessories. It was her mother, who'd guzzled a much more lethal fistful of little things. When I heard him leave that night I walked out to the kitchen, where my mother was sitting with the pack of cigarettes he'd taught her to suck on, turning them around and around in her skinny red-tipped hand. 'He told me she was crazy. I knew that girl had to get it from somewhere.' She sighed at me and a long thread of smoke came out and spread across her face. 'The woman's out of her mind. I can't believe I let you stay there.'

But I didn't think she was crazy. I thought she had it exactly right. Clearly a cocktail of Barbie doll shoes just wasn't going to do it.

V. THE SMALLNESS OF BONES

PENELOPE WATERS WAS A SMALL child sitting on a very large bed. The bedspread beneath her was red and man-made, the kind of material which women's bedjackets and nightgowns were also made of. Its edges curled into a sort of synthetic froth. Penelope liked to crawl underneath it and come up like a ghost in the mirror, her small face floating seriously beneath its red transparency. But the body of the bed-spread was thicker and quilted with scallop-edged diamonds. If you ran your finger over it, as you would if you were Penelope, at first it would almost feel like very soft skin — the kind of skin Penelope feels would be under the fingers of women on tele-vision, as they touch their faces with satisfied circles of thick white cream. Yet if Penelope closes her eyes and really listens to her fingers, the sensation of skin gives way and the bedspread then begins to feel net-like, as if she can find each tiny fibre crossing and recrossing itself to make the large red bed.

Her mother has just killed a dog and is weeping in three pieces. At least, this is what it seems like to Penelope, who always sits on the bed precisely at the angle to see three of her mothers in the mirror, and her own face folded up funnily along the hinge. This is her ritual in the mornings: to follow the red map of the bed, and watch her mother opening and closing the various boxes on her dresser, opening her eyes up like pretty flowers with kindergarten paint. Sometimes her mother moves one eye very close to the mirror, pulling open or stretching straight its lid in an ugly way, and her mouth also stretches down in a way that suddenly changes the shape of her face. The bones beneath her mother's face seem suddenly to get very close to the surface, and this reminds Penelope of a story she's been told, by the-Tuesday-morning-Bible-woman, a story with a jawbone in it somewhere. The Bible-woman had a picture of that jawbone. It stuck cut-out to the felt-board amongst the long blue robes of the holy people in a very threatening way. The same blue people in their bed-sheet dresses would reappear in another morning's story, so she didn't really worry about them. But Penelope did worry about that jawbone. It looked like it was evil-grinning at the back of the Bible-woman's head, like it knew a different story to any one that she could tell you.

Whatever is under her mother's face is not at all like this. Penelope knows her mother's skeleton is made of something much lighter and thinner — like the lid of the jewel-box or the perfume bottle with its puff-puff top. But Penelope has seen her mother cry in the mirror a few times now, and so, although she is interested she sometimes wishes she could move on to the stage where her mother straightens her dress and uses a sigh to push herself up from the dresser. Then Penelope climbs to her queenish seat and plays with the jewel box, turning its tiny golden key and lifting out its tray. She is allowed to try things on and watch herself weighed down by amethysts, to loop and turn, loop and turn a very long string of pearls. But the one thing coveted by Penelope, more than any other treasure, is something which she cannot even wear. It is an opal, cold and oval, tucked inside a tiny-padded-yellow-silk case. Penelope, holding the opal until it is almost throbbing, pretends there is some kind of magical power closed up inside its broken rainbows, and that she will grow up to release it one day. That's bad luck, says her mother however, put that thing away. Penelope wonders why you would keep bad luck wrapped up so carefully in your dresser.

The eyes of the dead dog had looked a bit like the opal — as though they would be smooth when you touched them, as if you could hold them in your hand to warm them, like the buttons that make eyes on teddy-bears. There were even lashes, dog-lashes, poking out from around the eyes, quivering. Penelope sat for a long time with the dog and her mother on the road side. The dog wasn't dead at first and so they had picked it up and walked up the path to the nearest house where they thought its owners might live. I don't give a fuck, the man who opened the door had said. Stupid little shit, I knew it would get itself bowled one day. Penelope knew these were not the nice words people should use when something was dying. So she took the dog from her mother who was sobbing and saying I'm sorry, I'm sorry, to the man who was still saying, I don't give a fuck, take it away.

Penelope had sat on the roadside then, and the dog began to stop making its noises, which were deep as an opal, wet and round. Penelope was able to hold the dog and watch it becoming lighter and lighter, and observe the small place beneath its rib cage move in and out like another mouth. The head of the dog was almost white but its body was covered in small black pictures — one was of a tall man tipping his hat, another was a house on fire. Penelope knew there was nothing she could do once her three mothers started weeping, and so she sat and watched the dog, which didn't watch her back but seemed almost to be watching its own breath making the grinding sounds of leaving its body.

Her parents' argument takes place afterward in a room far, far away. Penelope's bedspread is pink and thick, it smells of winter coats and old shoeboxes, and it's patterned in raised velvet waves. When Penelope is sleeping in it she has to try very hard to think 'waves,' because 'snakes' are the things that slip in her mind at night-time. The darkness does not leave behind the colour pink to protect her, and 'pink' in your head is of course no match for 'snakes'.

Words are always arriving like that: her parents' room, at this moment, for instance, is full of words like 'snakes'.

Do you know how god-awfully ridiculous it is, the bloody vet's wife running around town, knocking down small animals? Don't you care how it looks?

Penelope's father was the vet. Sometimes, lately, when her mother spent the day crying, or waiting to cry, Penelope had to follow him, out over the quilted field to where an animal lay talking about its pain somewhere below her gumboots. Inside her boots it was greasy and cold and if you looked down the long pink tube you could just see the place where her toes made curls of dirt. That's what she looked at: dirt patterns, cold patterns.

Not at the red strings where too much animal covered over her father's arm.

Don't you care how you look anymore?

Penelope thinks this is very odd. Her mother mostly spends days in the mirror checking carefully on how she looks as her dress moves past on her three long bodies, or reading glossies that give her hot shiny lists on how to care more. If she comes out of the mirror wrong, as she did with the silver stilettos, Penelope's father will help her, sending her six jerky legs back to her bedroom.

Are you trying to make me a joke? Have you got nothing to say for yourself?

Penelope's mother has nothing to say for herself except a throat noise. It is thick and fluttery, like the red bedspread pulled out into air, shaken.

I said, don't you care how it looks?

Penelope's father had told her she had to look. She didn't want to be like her mother, did she: soft, too soft to stand up to things.

Penelope did not say that it was the hard things inside her that worried her, the pictures that were standing up inside her, the words.

When she had to look down at the animal she worried that a bible-shaped bone would come crackling out in her father's hand.

Instead what slid out was necklace-shiny, a pouch and a leash of blue-yellow plastic, as if her schoolbag had been melted and packed with floating sticks.

Penelope's mother had brought her schoolbag. Penelope had been in the garden when her mother had walked out carrying it, as if it were going to struggle, up by her ribs. Penelope had sat in the front seat, without her mother asking her, and her mother had bent in through the window and put the schoolbag on Penelope's lap. Penelope had been looking through it when the dog ran at the car, barking. There were strange things in it, and clever things: her ladybird stickers, her knucklebones, but also a folded raincoat and her underpants sprinkled with days of the week. Penelope liked to think of her mother, choosing these things from her little dresser, perhaps trying her bracelets on, working the elasticated beads up the bones of her wrist. That's what she'd been thinking of when the dog had made its last wet snap, and the car had stopped on the grass making swallowing sounds and her mother said I can't have. She'd been thinking of her mother, in the little mirror where there was only one of her.

Penelope's parents put her in her bedroom while they have their argument, because they think this will stop her listening. Of course Penelope knows that the opal that has given her special powers, has also given her the bad-luck gift of hearing every word her parents say. In fact, this time while they're arguing, Penelope thinks she can feel it, the opal, beating softly in and out inside its yellow case.

I'll be a laughing stock. I can't step out the door without you making a spectacle.

The words that Penelope knows already disappear quite quickly, but the ones that Penelope does not know remain.

Penelope doesn't know any meanings for the word *spectacle*, but it makes her think about the letterbox outside the angry man's house which said 39. While Penelope was busy looking at the pictures on the cave of the dog's dark body, she suddenly woke up to find her mother sitting at her side, and the dog no longer singing. *Where do you think we should put it?* said her mother. Penelope didn't know. And so she walked with it slung in her arms back to the door where the man had answered. *I told you I don't fuckin' want it,* he said. So Penelope looked around the garden for a place to put the dog down. But it was mostly cutty-grass, and since the dog hadn't wanted to let go much of its warm blood it seemed to Penelope that he should be allowed to keep it. The letter box was the large old kind with a big stand for the milk bottles, and a metal flap for the mail that has a voice you can feel in your face bones whenever you pull it out on colder mornings. But Penelope found that although the dog was small he wouldn't fit in anywhere, so she laid him over the letter box roof and had to balance him carefully, finding that the heavier weight of his head pulled over the snake of his back legs. It seemed to Penelope to be many times the dog slid over the tin roof scratching. But eventually he lay down, and Penelope tried not to feel him watching as she walked back to where her mother was already sitting behind the wheel.

Penelope knew which way they were going when her mother turned the mirror, painting her mouth and eyes back into the silky space above her jawbone.

VI. CUTS

WHEN A CUSTOMER GOT OUT his penis, as some of the clientele had been known to do, the women of Diamante Salon kept up the chatter, their gossip ringing and glinting. An outsider would never detect, from their chirps and giggles, their chic, pert talk, that the hairdressing girls had put into operation a cool defensive strategy. Once or twice, a beaded wrist might twitch at the cape, a quick, glib puff, trying to rustle the silver fabric back across the offending organ. But otherwise their snipping and oiling never ceased: heads were divided into sections, dark tangents of hair were pulled tight, the graphed scalp, a fatty white, came up in tiny coordinates. The customer leaned back, felt the hairdresser's fingers worming against his lobes, moist and agile, and lowered his zip a little deeper, manoeuvred a little more nervy sac to the side. The women's talk, chiming, lenient, sprinkled across him, left him lulled. In their mirrors, his relayed cock looked gallant, split into gleaming clones. Staring back at him from altitude, it gave him a sense of adventure, empire. 'Has Priscilla booked in for her permanent?' slipped past in the women's conversation; he barely heard.

But that was it: the code, the trigger, a phrase every new girl was drilled in when she joined the crew. 'Has Priscilla booked in for her permanent?' drew no gasps, no shudders, not even a glance: but amidst the salon chat, one of the women would slip through the clinking-gem curtain, cut through the alley at the shop-back, ring the police from the neighbouring store and arrive back at the salon with the menswear shop owner to detain the underdressed man until the cops could arrive to take statements.

The talk continues, but with an added hiss, as the women

wait for the policeman. They are jumpily vivacious, their eyes are outlined in hard blue channels, and their teeth, through slick red lips, mime a bright, contrived anger. 'Oh, what I wouldn't like to do,' they say, gnashing, 'what I wouldn't like to do.'

*

Serena's mouth, to her great regret, suffers from a lack of definition.

Definition, the latest magazines in the salon say, is the key to great lips. This winter season, Serena's copy of *Cosmetropolis* warns, a mouth without definition is like a rugby field with no goal line.

Serena is a thin woman and hardly makes the curtain tingle as she vanishes regularly behind it to reapply a pink, distinctive mouth. When most of today's customers are blow-dried, back-combed, expelled, and the salon is closed temporarily, the women arrange themselves squeakily in the swivel-chairs, but Serena feels she's out of place. The other women take custody of their flasher with a solemn collective glamour; Serena feels like a cleaning woman in a scene from *Charlie's Angels*. She slides out the back for a lippy-break, blotting a crisp fuchsia contusion in between the allotted plum outline.

Serena does realise she should count her blessings; not so very long ago she was counting her teeth. The young Serena, sprouting her adult teeth, had produced twice what she needed, double rows of canines forking her gum at angles both savage and comic. Tooth after tooth had been uprooted, brace after brace had been welded on: *when are they letting your teeth out of prison*, her father had cracked, thinking it a new joke each time.

Most of Serena's memories centre on her mouth, its treachery, its violent white fruit. She watches it in the mirror today: it looks flat, orderly, suspiciously bland. On the night

of her first brace, Serena remembers, she had to babysit for the
Forsyths; when she arrived at the house she had not yet
mastered the iron negotiations of a smile. The Forsyths opened
the front door, greeted her; she grinned in reply and her lip was
snared on the black bars. She remembers the mortification of
having to put her handbag down and use her fingers to uncurl
her upper lip, working it down over metal, hook by hook,
already dripping.

That night, when Mr Forsyth drove her home, there could
be no kissing. He didn't seem to mind, but the lack of a
blowjob caused him some annoyance. Serena had felt him
search for alternatives, rolling her hips in their acid-wash
denim, his thumb kneading in toward her anus, stubby,
inquiring. But Serena, even with a heavily engineered face and
no prospect of future boyfriends, had drawn the line. Mr
Forsyth said that he knew a good dentist; *maybe we can spring
your teeth for one night,* he laughed. *For good behaviour. Out
on parole.*

Serena draws the line now too, Persistent Purple, topped
with Hot Whipped Rose. But she can't help thinking that the
lips left impacted on the tissue, their O-print of greasy
scratches, have more definition than the wan split she wears
back into the salon. She grimaces with her workmates; her
mouth feels ineffective and tidy. Sometimes Serena feels a
twinge of nostalgia for the thrust of those lost wolvish incisors.

*

Mrs Newland is having her set, a rigid Wednesday-fortnight
appointment, and no display of a scruffy set of privates is going
to upset her booking. This is what she tells the women when
they lift the hood of her dryer. The women try to describe
the scenario; they struggle to find euphemisms befitting her
blue-rinsed hair. They offer to schedule a new slot, urge a
complimentary triangle of chiffon toward her curlers; no
whippersnapper's whatnot is going to cut short her drying time,

Mrs Newland informs them. Why on earth should a decent woman's timetable be overturned by some upstart's inappropriate airing of his personal region? Certainly not, she's keeping her curlers frying, her helmet decidedly on.

Mrs Newland keeps her eyes on the invader, all the same.

*

The man is attempting to evade chat, feign bravado, as Trixie quizzes him. A little of his member is still softly breaching his Bermuda shorts.

'Gavin,' the man finally says.

'And does this gentleman also have a name, Gavin?'

'What?'

'Are you of the order of men who bestow little pseudonyms on their privates, Gavin? Does it have an alias? Does the wee fellow come with an extensive list of aka's? Is it wanted in several states? Has it been leading a double life?'

Trixie leans forward; her purple blouse opens. The wrinkled margin between her breasts is displayed, dappled with tan-lotion. The women, all silent, follow her movements, impressed with her mix of flirtatious violence, the subtext of ferocity informing the slant of Trixie's seductively plucked brows.

'I'd like to suggest, Gavin, off-hand and confidentially, that you tuck it away. Shall we call him John Thomas, for convenience's sake? John Thomas, I'm sure, wouldn't mind retiring, just for the sake of conversation.'

But the man doesn't move.

Trixie regards him, swivels, jauntily, back and forth on her silver seat.

'You seem, Gavin, to be disinclined for the gland to miss our sparkling conversation, and no one, least of all our menswear shop-minder here, is keen to manually compel you. Now, this may come as a surprise to you, Gavin, but your modus operandi is not entirely unknown to us. We are certainly not amused, but neither are we intimidated, by having to sit in a room, speculating on personal objects which we would rather were upholstered. If we have to converse in the presence of little J.T., we can. So, Gavin, tell us, what you do, when you're not getting your tender parts out to entertain unsuspecting hairdressers?'

'I don't like to say.'

'Well, frankly, Gavin, it seems just a shade unusual for a man with his organ out to suddenly blush when the conversation turns to the nature of his employment.'

The man remains silent. He tries a glare, but his expression is more one of stupor.

'I once went out with a man who was likewise secretive about his work,' comments Trixie. 'And do you know what it was he did, Gavin? He was — and there's really no other way to say it, Gavin — a horse wanker. I don't delude you. When the horse stud required the siring of champions enacted, this man held the position of having to masturbate the stallions. Things went rather badly after he confided that. In short, Gavin, I laughed. I believe I outright snorted. The thing that popped into my head, Gavin, was what his curriculum vitae would look like. Can you imagine it: *1981 professional horse wanker.*'

Trixie pauses while the women settle, then resumes with diminished bite.

'The most astonishing thing was, he seemed to think it superior to hairdressing.'

*

Abigail, gathering up the scissors and popping them into a pot of solution, is thinking of finding Jesus. Twice now he's appeared in her dreams. At least, she's almost certain it's Jesus; he does bear an alarming resemblance to the man who works in the adjacent fish and chip shop.

Abigail stops at the fish and chip shop most nights, picks up a steaming newspaper roll. She likes to tear the top of it open, as she walks up the railway line to her flat; she likes to tease herself with a few salty tips, a fleck or two of batter. But when she gets home she unwraps the parcel and fully considers the ends of fish batter the way she used to watch clouds when she was little, searching for visionary shapes, mystical occurrences. It seems no less probable to Abigail that holy omens should be pressed into fried fish than into the frothing molecules that cluster the horizon. Besides the fish seems much more particular to her; she orders ahead most nights.

Church has disappointed Abigail however. What strikes her is the plainness of the women. Abigail, lurking in the foyer on her recent visits, has been embraced by women, welcomed, pressed by talcum-powdered hands; but what she has noticed is the odour of scone which emanates from their cardigans, the tea-coloured base to their teeth, and, of course (worst of all), their incidental hair. Nondescript hair clings in thin colourless lines to their skulls like lines of scripture. During the service, the minister has earnestly talked of what lovers of God must give up: Abigail hasn't heard the details, but it seems clear from the women's presentation that mascara and hair mousse are among the items to be sacrificed. Abigail doesn't like to admit it to herself, and she certainly didn't confide it in the ring of pale, quivering women that prayed over her after the last service, but this is posing a significant block to her conversion: if it comes down to a choice between Jesus and Maybelline, Abigail has real worries that her impulse will be cosmetic rather than Christian.

What she had liked about her dream of Jesus was that his face and robe were flanked by locks of thick and well-conditioned hair. In the dream she was standing with him: they were in the salon, and Abigail was handing him the white paper tablets and the colour-coded perm rods to wrap and roll the customer. When she thinks about Jesus now, his image is tinted, astringent. The halo around him is as sleek as gel, and he leaves behind a scent of neutraliser.

*

On the outside, there's a point when you no longer look in, but stare further out . . .

That's what Mary wants to tell the hairdresser, strange brittle strings of sound, phrases that have slipped past meaning, but somehow link and glimmer in a secret part of her. *There are two kinds of women in this small town: those who wear make-up and those who do not. My children will not survive with the first kind . . .* Instead, she sits, extends her neck over the grooved black plastic basin, and stares at the face, frosted and lucid, of the woman who is slowly stealing her husband.

You stare further out, out the door of your own house, past your children's bikes, their swing, their swing, their climbing tree, the trees unclimbed in the neighbour's garden, the fruit dripping to its soft extinction on the concrete . . . The woman's fingers are spread on her scalp, feel cold and obsessive in their fan of movement. *Further out, further out because you know there'll be a point when you turn and you'll no longer have what you've belonged to, what's fallen behind you, the house, the hallway, the new blue curtains, even the light in the children's faces as they ask you for breakfast, it's all blowing away beyond your frozen back as the new woman walks up the drive . . .* She feels fingernails: in a job like this you'd imagine you'd have to keep them trimmed; when Mary had the babies she'd had to cut hers back, deep, to the quick. Many times, working tender bellies into cloth, collarbones under woollen singlets, bread or rice into mouths in soft wet pods, the babies had cried out at her. Mary's nail marks shone back at her from their bodies, random and glowing. *Further out, abandoned cars, sheds, sheds, the railway lines, the sea, pulled tight as a page of your husband's handwriting meant for another woman . . .*

But Mary says nothing. There's no disturbance: she breaks nothing, she shrieks nothing. They ask her sympathetically, gently, to go, but it's not because of her. When the man with his fly pulled to the side watches Mary leaving, her hair is still wet, uncut, a dark aimless track down onto her rose-embroidered cardigan.

*

Sally is tired. She boils the Zip, watching the mist spitting in the long glass stem, the rust on the valve that one of the girls has tried to scratch her name in. She's tired because she's spent all weekend moving April out of her house, dragging box after half-burst box down ninety-seven steps (she counted), and not even very well cut steps, but the kind of sloping stock-track bastard, half clay, half sand. Three friggin' times her jandal had skidded off with a rubbery will of its own, and Sally had landed smack on her tailbone, frypan, stilettos, diaphragm splayed out in the manuka.

And now, to end all, she's making a bloody cup of tea for a bloke with his goat sack out. She's tempted (and this temptation rises, buzzes in her neck as the Zip starts whistling) to fake a trip-up and pour the whole thing in his lap. Circumcision, she thinks, courtesy of Bell Tea-bags. Drink Bell Tea and you'll be feeling alive little man.

But Sally stands behind the curtain for a little longer, has a slurp of her own tea first. Up and down those damn steps, she'd known April wasn't really moving, that Sally, obedient, weary Sally was just part of the I'm-really-leaving-show, that Brett was expected, eventually, and after the contents of a six-pack had loosened his emotions, to follow them up and down, pleading, putting on the cute-but-psycho routine, remove boxes from Sally's mini, hump them with grunts of sweaty love back up the steps. On her last trip into the house, as she wound up the cord of the sandwich maker, Sally had not been surprised to catch sight of the two of them in the mirrored cabinet, Brett lifting April onto the bathroom sink, running his hands into her Adidas pants, and fingering her to the chant of *you know you're staying, say you're staying April.*

Sally had walked down the steps, driven off in her car, still packed with April's boxes. And the thing Sally thought of, that did surprise her, was how April had crept into her bed last time she'd left her boyfriend. How April had lifted Sally's T-shirt, and lain her head just above her hips, so heat shot in a thousand tremors into a mesh of muscles Sally didn't know she had.

*

She could kill him. She could will him dead. She'd done it before, when she was little. She'd been new at the school, she even remembers what she was wearing, a red corduroy dress, yellow and red striped tights and a dark green headband. The teacher had asked her what she was like at her old school, was she clever at maths, and she'd said, she was in purple for reading and orange for maths, the top groups. But then, the boy next to her sent her a note during maths, a fuzzy scrap which read *I get the first pash with new girls, meet you at lunch in the toilets*, and she hadn't been able to get the division to round out right, there were numbers slipping, sticking out, and when the teacher marked it, he laughed at the idea of her being a clever girl, said you must be colour blind.

Laughed until she cried and wished him dead.

And that afternoon he'd taken the boys out onto the soccer field. He'd dropped, slack and soundless, at the edge of the game, so they'd played on for minutes before the ball came back his way, kicked past his cold blue face.

She'd stood, combing, snipping, piped out: 'Is Priscilla booked in for her permanent?' She'd waited for the chink of the diamante-curtain, the swish, like a magic wand, that let her know she would be saved. But it was a long time to wait: in the man's hair, as she sprayed and divided it, were flaps of dandruff, fleecy cream slots of scalp. Time passed, elongated: the man's head, hovering by her breasts, was a black and white diagram. It seemed to swell, take on the leathery shimmer of a soccer ball.

I could kill him, she thought.

*

'Maybe he's not all there.'

The other women look at Dorothy.

'Well. It's just, he doesn't say much.'

'Gavin,' says Trixie, 'My colleague Dorothy is inquiring whether you're all there. No offence to little John Thomas, of course, but it is a fair question.'

Dorothy can tell by the man's red neck that he is, at least, intelligent enough to be experiencing intense hate for Trixie.

She sits back down. She rubs her thumb, quietly, up and down her plastic apron.

Long ago, Dorothy had consulted doctors. Her son could be capable of doing this, they said. Her little boy, they told her, was no longer pliant, could constitute a threat. Dorothy's husband, long before they moved and she came to the Diamante, had led her boy along the path to an institution where such threats — large, smiling, playful threats like Dorothy's son — could be contained.

Every view of sky in the place was strapped down by long white bars. Dorothy closed her eyes after visits, sat in her car on the side of the road, and always it seemed those bars had painted their shadows in her. They droned, down her eyelids.

She told herself the bars were just as well: it had been windows that did it, his taking to suddenly thudding off down the street. He didn't even know to creep, just clopped off, crushing through flowers past the letterbox, laughing back at her, jumbling away, as if he was pretending, their animal game. But fast, faster than Dorothy could chase him. When she caught him he would be fixed, his big hands throbbing at somebody's pane, some woman cornering herself away from the lamplight, clawing together her garments.

Dorothy remembers looking down into his eye when he was a baby: billows of silver light, like smoke in stitches, hung in from the ring of his iris.

Dorothy has to face the fact that her son is not all there.

But now that her son is no longer with her Dorothy feels that she's not all here either.

*

Trevor, from the menswear shop, runs a bet with his staff members. The bet involves the number of days it will take him to get his end away with any new hairdresser (if she is worth hooking into) who starts at the Diamante Salon. Squatting his large walk-shorted buttocks on a silver stool he regards the new girl. He can't remember her name, but he thinks to himself, this must be the second time a flasher has inadvertently helped on Trevor's quest for getting his leg over a hairdresser.

*

Before she was a salon owner Trixie used to be a whore. Trixie uses the word when describing her past life, stubbornly, parodically, *whore*. *Whore* she says, even though, with the vast lexicon she displays in conversation (a flashy vocabulary she picked up from clientele who were loaded and cerebral), you know she could label the profession something much more enticing and exotic.

Trixie knows the very moment she stopped being a whore, she'll tell you. One man, after they'd transacted their erotic business standing up, had lain down with her, listened to her complaining about the flies in her rented room. Flies, there were, tiny noiseless houseflies no bigger than airborne seeds, but the type of flies who were driven to human flesh, who landed and drizzled on you. They'd wake you in the night, a ruffle on your mouth, sometimes catch in your hair and thud there, tiny dizzy ruptures that sent you insane, swiping at your own head. But this man had got up, dressed, gone down to the dairy, come back with a can of flyspray. They'd lain on the bed for the rest of the afternoon, naked, talking, sharing the spray, bursts of toxin jetting into the air above their bodies.

And the moment she stopped being a whore was this,

Trixie will tell you. The man turned to her and said, Do you think there's anyone else in the world, man and woman, lying on the bed, exactly like us, this very minute, doing this?

*

Abigail offers to nip out and get everyone some fish and chips. The policeman is taking a very long time; surely the other women must be hungry?

The other women look at each other. They've withdrawn, discussed Abigail before, chatted over strategies. They're not hungry, they tell her.

As she leaves, they comment blithely, How you can live on fish and chips and never put on any weight, I don't know. But the tone in which the remark is delivered, bored and incisive, lets Abigail know that the women realise exactly how she does it.

This time, after she's brought up the mass of fluted grease and yellow mash, Abigail feels faint to the point of prophecy, leans her forehead against the concrete cubicle wall. Jesus approaches, passing her a new package wrapped in paper, which Abigail, already ravenous, grabs at haggardly, starts to strip off. But as fast as she tears off strands of paper more pages seem to wrap the parcel, warm pulp binding and sealing the contents in thick dark bands of growth. And as she tears she sees the headlines passing her eye as if in slow motion, finds herself reading coil after coil of paragraphs, long continuous columns: a list of everything she's eaten since birth.

She washes her face when it's over. Down to skin and clear eyelash. It's not so bad. She thinks she may go back to church.

*

What Kelly hadn't expected was the blood. *The volume, the compound of it. The spread of somebody's mother's bed doused and rippled in so much of Kelly's blood.* She'd hunted him down for months. She'd practically been stalking him. She'd seen him, in the spotlight, shooting rats out at the dump one night, and she'd had him marked down for her first time ever since. *Blood conducting itself into seams, accruing along the weft of velvet.* The party had been at some anonymous high-school kid's house. She lured him to the parents' bedroom, waving a gin bottle at him, trying to exotically lick around its lid. She'd practically exposed herself, she thinks, looking now at the man in the salon. *Even when he climbed out of her, and she sat up, trying to clench herself, blood still rolling from her trunk, and him, not trying to help her staunch it, but trying to slap it off himself. As if it were acid, as if it were animal.* He'd gone out, still half-smeared with it, into the throng of drunken kids, to find some girl to deal with it. Any girl would do, to deal with it, just not him. He brought back three, young faces Kelly recognised from the days before she left school, slim, blonde, sincere children who padded her, patted away at the mess, whispered in biased sugary little voices. *Her blood: its red lamination everywhere.*

It was weeks ago now, but the town was still talking. The story had flowed from the house with an artery's speed. Talking about her, but never to her. Not even him.

And this morning, on the way to the salon, she'd gone past the op-shop. Displayed in the window was the long red dress she'd been wearing that night, its neckline flapping, its skirt pinned out into fins, its spectrum of satin buckled over the pelvis with a sequence of plump glassy hearts. *Salvation Red Dot Sale*, the sign said.

*

Mary waits in the street. She sees her husband coming, holds up a wrist. On the collar of his uniform is a muted trimming of pink.

'I didn't wash it properly,' she says. When he first started in the job and brought home his shirts with their strange marks of violence, Mary had always kept the uniform separate, pushed in the laundry corner. She had needed to keep it distinct from the porous shapes of her babies' gowns, their tender damp pinafores. Now she no longer noticed; the mass of clothing, the years, in the small room converged. 'Still someone's blood.'

Or lipstick, she thinks.

He brushes down her fingers. The ring of woven thread the children have tied on her hand is pulled crooked, almost slips off. He touches it, a question. Mary nods, winds its lapse of colours over her index finger.

'For friendship, the girls said,' Mary explains. 'They're all wearing them. They spend hours making them.'

'A job on at the salon,' he says. It's a lank voice, and he jolts his head tiredly at the window. His every move understated. 'Better not keep them waiting.'

'Okay,' Mary says.

But he stands and watches his wife, her figure slenderly retreating. He notices her hair is wet, hangs in a fused pelt down her back. But then she reaches the end of his vision, where the road turns into a hollow, and the texture of her body slides from his horizon with a smudge.

*

'Know what they should call this place,' Gavin says to the policeman.

'What's that, mate?' he asks.

'Cutting Remarks. Fucking Cutting Remarks.'

'That's very good, Gavin,' Trixie snaps. 'That's very astute of you. But what you still fail to comprehend, Gavin, what you show no sign of absorbing, is the fact that you're in a room with complex women. Complex, multi-dimensional women, Gavin. Women with longings, women with opinions. Intricate, unpredictable girls.'

'And here's what should really concern you. Here's what it

would most pay you to contemplate,' she says to Gavin's back as the cop leads him out. 'Women with scissors.' The door rings shut.

*

Dorothy thinks, on her way home she'll stop quietly down to the beach. He's never been to this beach, this new-town beach, but she tells him of it, on visits. Her son walks ahead of her, steps heavy, one arm always held stiffly out to run the perimeter of silver trees. Their branches leave, not cuts, but delineations up the thick flesh of his arm, and when they return to the home he hovers from face to face, showing the striations to everyone.

Last time she'd told her son of how the beach has a creek etched over it, a stem of fresh water, and wading through it she'd found a string of baby eels. They were gliding in a pale rock's ditch, allies shivering in a single cluster, no more solid than worms. I picked one up, she said to her son, you wouldn't believe how brave your mother was: I picked up the biggest and I let him slither about in my palm. Like a little boy, I was. She had seen the spine like a long black pen stroke, the pink crimp of gills. A tiny vibrating drain which may be a heartbeat.

Like a little boy, I was.

Dorothy won't stay long at the beach; she doesn't stop long on her visits either. She's anxious to get home to her husband, his shabby, valid presence in the armchair, the density of his voice as he barks incoherently at the TV. Her husband had been resolute on the subject of her son. He was a man with limits, and he was not the boy's father. But he did cry when he came home that day, after leading her son down the narrow path, after being the first of them to click shut the long humming gate. He did cry. Dorothy remembers seeing the tears: three, dull and flesh-coloured, travelling slowly down into his beard.

Dorothy wishes she could have taken them from his face

and somehow preserved them. She wishes that tears could be somehow hardened, congealed. There should be a recipe. She could keep them on her here, in the corner of the salon, she could hold their composite light clicking in her apron like a broken set of beads. She could slip them out; she could watch their corona, just for a moment, trickle through the room's many mirrors.

VII. THE UNDERSTANDING OF SILENCE

1.
Beneath
the water she hated
the sight of his hands

2.
Undress.   You have seen your old
skin, sugar bag   a cotton shed.
Integers   of memory
glisten,   days are broken into
syllables, your hands   are wet with
fruit. Fluent   green in the full-
tongued trees,   the red couch
with its fat   arms shredded, cat's claw,
marital love   impatiently made.
Curtsey   cracking princess I have
made you   a hair net of words.

3.
The memory lets
itself in. It touches
the bones of
your face while you
are sleeping. It has
already chosen
a path through the house.

4.

Cold you said came up   through
the floorboards. Lovesongs   could not
have been a remedy.   Photographs
still less.

5.

The rain decides
what you see for the night. Your
small town gets even
smaller. We bring the pram in
from the front of the house
the washing in from the back

6.

an aerial view of the house   wears her
white dress. In the hot ditch   of hills
she watches   their muscularity tighten
her evening.   A child applied to her
lace, her redness.   Over his small
mouth she watches   the black altitude
of church bells over   the town.

7.

She could not
sleep until he left
that elegiac space beside
the bed.

8.
If you owned the story you could choose
to finger its spine. Its heart   is rough
with many voices. There   are empty
hands on all the trees.   And there is
a low white beach   that makes a bone
where memory is breaking.   It does not
happen here   where it happens.
It reaches   the shore in shapes in
later years.

9.
The woman remembers
        she was there.

        She has books
to tell her differently.

        Once is always
a long time ago.

10.
villa   in a street of blue
with tides   the sound that no one
mentioned. Each day   you renewed
your wish   to pull the house around
to face the sun.   Seaweed, liver oil,
smells of your hysteria   & a salt-
coloured box.   Silver collections
of pity &   a white church
closed inside you.

11.

A single image enters her eye. The
sky is below, her memories
in it like water. The people and
the trees are strokes of shadow
hanging from the ground.

12.

A habit of listening to   the lonely
shallows of   your blood. Your
expectation   slows it. Take off
your shoes   wade out my angel.

13.

This
is the heart's accomplishment. It
moves through its sequence
precise in its assonance. Like
leaving it stays
in the present
tense as you empty
the house.

rules for teachers (1915)

1. You will NOT marry during the term of your contract.

You have to eat
their gardens

their calcography
of yellow nouns

your vegetable lace
is not a mouthful
you can rustle with desire

a pouch of verbs
you dry to frills
against your sombre finger

2. You will NOT keep company with men.

you teach them that
the heart is lambent

loops of dust
along the walls of night

the song of fingernails
& circumstance

a prim ignition

3. You MUST be home between the hours of 8pm and 6am unless attending a school function.

the iconography
of blooms

> *when you dance your boots*
> *cut new feet*

lessons of how beauty closes
even roses' heads break

> *yellow claws have grown*
> *their polka*

in the diagnosis
of your lush iambic doom

> *your ankles are home*
> *like scone dough*

4. You may NOT loiter downtown in ice cream parlours.

the diction
of your wild mouth

a soft mosaic
of this sugar, resinous
with muffled cold

> *you watch him*
> *from the base of it*
> *the wistful licks at wrinkled cone*

the mortal syrup
under budded glove

5. You may NOT travel beyond the city limits without the permission of the chairman of the board.

buckle my shoe
the wind has milled your blood

you are an infidel of supple waters
loose hair swum by lamplight

>   *they know your eyes are coastal*
>   *see theism and distance in them*

solvent pressures of your skin
against the quiet field

6. You may NOT ride in a carriage or automobile with any man unless he is your father or brother.

fallen in the sand
the stars of fur
the burst of lice & feather

flanks of harbours
pushing past your veil

trinkets of gooseflesh
belts of stringy shell
the sea has sold her

7. *You may NOT smoke cigarettes.*

you learn to breathe
against the heavy spine of sheets

their cotton pulled to phantoms
in the lavish soiled air

an exhalation
psalmic as the smell of him
a vein of coiling light

within the mattress
where you slid your index of the supine words
diaphanous was there

8. *You may NOT dress in bright colours.*

but do they think their signature
of serge won't leave you
itching after something?

the glossology
of knots against your fasted skin

the fatal shades
are knit with chafing
sampling these pleats of blood

> to *fabricate,* you teach your pupils
> raps of your recited bone

a map of ligaments
he held against you

9. *You may UNDER NO CIRCUMSTANCES dye your hair.*

they are cutaneous
ribbons he's left

> *I am an envelope*
> longhand tumbles
> from my body like thread

there is no polish in my hair
but ventricles of net
against my face

> *a codicil*
> *to my strict dreams*

10. *You must wear AT LEAST two petticoats and your dresses must not be any shorter than 2 inches above the ankles.*

each slush of skirts a slow

cloistration, teach them that
a covered walk

                              contours of lassitude
                              between you & the thick bayou of clay

an ocean broken through
his eye with corpuscles of shadow

                              the loss of him
                              is pulmonary

how shall you
conceal your quilt of cells?

the poet on honeymoon tasting water

*
& during
those years she
tried to step
out of his
shadow but
in the publicity
stills there
was always the shade
of a hand
across her
mouth.

*
later that
night Icarus kissed
her & told
her the secret
of falling
in two.

the MaryS

I am reading   a woman. We are
staying up late   alone. She has
the house holed   in her mouthing
      out   a gory oracle

She has taken herself   off she has taken her
self over.   She expects
parameters   along the soft
knock of   my tongue. We dust the
page for widowed   skin. She laughs and her long
book   fails me

Explain   your sestina to me
while we share   garments for heartless
dolls. We   put them to
sleep in alphabetical destiny   teach ourselves
sleeplessness
inventory

She is anxious about   the interiority
of kisses. She is   wearing a house
a coat of many   hours

The trees   are here.
They keep the darkness   branching in her
iris. The transaction   happens when she's not
concentrating on the cruelty   of his hands.

            The hand that rocks   the cradle rocks
                    the cradle   rocks the cradle.
      She melts down   butter over the nuptial
                                                wound

I lay her face   down. Her spine
arcs   a history

a sonnet halved

i.
So temporal, our house inside this night
the hills like old clothes folded around us

smelling of selves we wore out in the past.
This dwelling of wet wood is all that our

memories have been building, the damp cloth
lining your eye a black out, your loud heart

hard at its boundaries of darkness.

ii.
Finally you reach the end of the house
near walls of slow white lilies — somnolent

thick-figured, they pretend not to be wild.
Later, you think, you'd have to believe

in each other; for now you've answered
the silence by settling love in the

bedroom, the shadows in gardens swollen
around the house. The soft hieroglyph of

his body is now alone in itself
on the summer grass — as he rolls to you,

its secret patterns are like sheet music
over his back. Your marriage has taken

to edging apart. Hard-valved, the lilies
know their black knuckles gleam beneath the ground.

anatomy of dancing with your future wife

1.
You do not say, the flowers
are like a bullet wound. They cost you
a packet and now they're mulch on her chest.
A corsage of blood.

2.
Six stone steps to the local.
On the third one a good mate stops you.
He asks you to let him know about redheads.
If it's true about the hair, down there.

3.
Six lost babies will slip past
that mould of bone you press your good suit
up against tonight. Two dates later in the dark you learn
it is a sculpted handful and she feels
like candlewax inside.

4.
For one or many reasons
the waist seam of her gown
is fishline.

5.
A pause in the music
lets you smell your breath
in the helix of her ear. Some men singing
drop from planes. Cliff Richard never marries.

6.

You called her a couple of days after
the dog died. Internal injuries, your Dad said.
That's what the little mug gets for chasing tyres.
You couldn't shift it from the crust of shit
it kept leaving on the shed floor. Its ribcage
swam up and down in its chest. Her eyes,
like the dogs, are the colour of lager.

7.

If you were lost on a desert island,
which item of makeup would you take? Your future wife
answers, concealer. You know she understands
the yellow plugs of pores. You look at the magazine and not
into the graffiti of her best friend's eyes.

8.

Through the shortcut to the hall
there are clots of inkweed. You'll remember this:
one leaf, a jellied bruise of seed
like a spoonful of roe.

9.

At the base of her neck
a brooch of veins that looks like a knot
from your scout book. You don't see her lose them.
They don't let you in.

the view from the new house

the first night in the new house
you perform an autopsy:
watching yourself in its windows
to make sure they can hold you in.

the hills are outside
your kitchen window
like a body under blankets.

you have a garden now
full of things you cannot name.

the house has a voice of its own
which you unlock
by living here listening;
the baby lies in his crib explaining
wordlessness to the song-webbed walls.

later that night in bed
you think you can see
its brown ribs breathing.

you keep expecting the hills
to move in the night.

HER BODY RISES

small parts of my family's body

What you remember about her is her toes. Her husband had to cut small holes in her house shoes, always pink or red. Her toes were yellow, the colour of skin which has lived without sun unbreathing under leather (kiss it better) or in a cast. They are bent in a way you never imagined the human body could manage. More beautiful than lotus crushed with a stone, the nail looks like a stone, trying to take over the rest of her feet. To you this seems like the curse of a fairytale, but she doesn't believe in fairytales and merely says 'Shoes in my day' and (slow flowering) words like winklepickers and bunions. You love her and you steal her shoes every time you visit, wearing them around the house, where your feet don't touch the sides.

she has seasons in her circle a bracelet of silver fish thin
songs & in small places where she puts her hands the
dinner bell bird cage charms a teaspoon left over to
tell her you have eaten the silence china clean & leaving
lets you see her reasons liking the icing of cakes the music
of dressing gowns holding the morning the sound of flour
on her hands the hovering of love

we find her writing like the wings of insects the light
ministration of birds her gingerbread hemming the
home our dresses needled with feeling herself sung
& the respiration of her stories swinging our skin to
school paspalum long ribboned with fingers bringing her
chrysalis her toothpick magic in the top of the airless jar

her discourse a lullaby card-trick foxtrot dancehall past all
honey hot shoes elizabeth pulling her music underground
seven years of letters from a lover in later days the children
turned the lawn to water she wouldn't get in never having
learned to come up under the dream swim back to her body
& stayed overdressed disturbed where deep ends took
her past herself & into history

this waltz ladies is alzheimer's time 3/fall 3/fall blanket &
butterfly vanity set her voice taken out each night & left
in a glass of cold water memories must be turned three times her
nets went heavy with breath in winter a whisper spent on the
heads of children desiccation brown leaves knitting her

HER BODY RISES

dreams a whole room living in the mist of her evening
forgiveness sounds like elizabeth rich arthritic angel wetting the
armchair at the door to herself she closes it without speaking

VIII. MOTHER'S LITTLE HELPERS

BEFORE SHE LEAVES FOR GIRL Guides, Eve checks her mother. Her mother's body makes a pool of shadow around itself on the bed, the clammy weight of her skin like a sea-creature, loose and pale in its shell. The white of her face in wet splits under her hair: Eve pokes it back with a finger. A few dark fibres pull like fishline out of the mouth, catching in teeth cracks. Eve leans in, a handful of her own hair cleared from neck and jawbone, pulse like a finger pushing up under her skin.

*

The Takewhero Community Hall is lit with candles. Eve always turns up early for this, to see the little Brownies joining, their stiff frocks scratching the paper flowers as they wander through the Magic Arch, up the carpet track to the fern-ringed pool. In its bed of crispy ponga, the Brownie pond is tinfoiled cardboard. But each little girl leans over, enchanted, seeing the Cinderella-ish girl in their handbook: 'Twist me and turn me and show me the elf/I looked in the water and there saw . . .'

The little girls stare into the pool at the bulging moon with slippery eye-holes. 'Myself': they manage to squeak with a clean breath.

Eve and a handful of other Guides are allowed to flank the ring of Brownies waiting by the pocked concrete toadstool which wobbles on the darkwood floor. Once, when Eve had been a Brownie, another girl had knocked off its dotted lid, soaking the roll of her ankle sock where it scraped through lace-edge into bone. Brown Owl, the hump of her mono-bosom buttoned stoutly over her belt, had bellowed up all the girls who'd earned their First Aid badge, and quizzed them over the squelchy leg in front of them. A circle of green-cheeked fairies with fright-sparkling eyes.

It had been Eve who'd held the chunk of bandage over the meaty burst. She had been able to write it down on her pinned-up list of '10 Ways In Which I Have Tried To Keep The Brownie Law', copying the perky little pictures from the handbook of girls pushing prams and vacuum-cleaners, with musical notes jumping around their hairstyles. At the bottom, Brown Owl's signature was thick red spikes: 'resourceful and unselfish'. But when Eve came into her room one day she found her mother's writing: 'A Brownie does a Good Turd Every Day'.

*

One knee lightly on the bed. Her mother's odour rolls on her, the mother-smell of sweat-and-flowers, like scented paper wrapped around meat. A thick cocktail that climbs on you, gets stuck in your hair like bubblegum. Closer in toward the mouth, sagging pinkly open, an oily drift of lipstick and sick.

'Are you a "change-daily girl" — clean blouse, undies, stockings, and hanky daily for that fresh feeling?' On that page of the handbook a camp washpan was propped in a stick-legged stand, a girl crouched in it brandishing the soap. Beside her was a list to help you take a 'good, hard look' at your grooming: 'Cleanliness — of yourself, of your clothing, of your home. Perhaps you can add some more? Of my . . . . . . Of my . . . . . . '

Eve's mother had filled in the spaces for her, using phrases from the handbook. 'Of my mounted gemstone. Of my bush' it now said.

*

When Eve was part of the Brownie pack, she had been in the Gnome Six: 'Here you see the laughing Gnomes, Helping mother in our homes.' On the Gnome sign a little stick-bodied Maori fairy danced with a broom. But Brown Owl had not seemed interested in frolicking with the household appliances. She didn't spend much time on their wildflowers poked into cracked old saucers of sand, or on the twisted stitches they'd snailed round the sticky-frill of their tea-tray mats. Brown Owl's big, raw body had seemed to gleam with enthusiasm for outdoors, for whacking up tea-tree ladders, for hurling blankets over a burning child. Her eyes were wrinkled in torchlight as she led them mystically round the hall — the thickfat shuddered under her arms as she jabbed out the semaphore flags.

Eve had not wanted to leave the Brownies. At her Flying Up ceremony, she'd walked into Tui's circle without a smile. Tui had a sleek mask of dark hair and white teeth, and her eyes were blue as the blindfolds in the game-bag. On Eve's first night Tui had demonstrated how to launder a woollen article, and hung its dripping carcass up on the line that Brown Owl had used to show them man-harness knot and donkey-hitches. Then Tui had held up a poster of potential household accidents, the woman balancing on a chair by a steaming jug with a trailing powercord. Poison, scissors and boiling water were on the rug by the beaming child.

When Tui spoke of the parts of the Little House Emblem which needed mother's guidance, Eve always thought that the bluebead eyes were on her. They were mean with shine.

*

Above the plastic survival kit the puckered skin of her mother's nipples, their mottled pink shifting like gooseflesh. Eve can even see the ring of fine hairs. She looks down into the kit until they are only a blur at the edge of her eyelid, but still she thinks she can see them moving.

It takes her a long time to find what she needs from the

tightly packed container. She takes out the water tablets, fishhooks, the aspirin, lays them on the bed. The pocket-knife, needle, matches, razor blade, cord. She thinks of the favourite poem her mother always recites at parties, a jerky sardonic list of ways to kill yourself, joking how rivers are soggy, ropes give. 'My résumé,' she says, and she always spits the last line, her loose breasts jolting for emphasis in her frayed blouse. Stuck to its thin surface her nipples are like eye smudges, clownish and teary. The room has always drained of sound, her voice is always overbright like TV women with squeezy bottles showing how *lemony freshness cuts dirt dead.* 'Well, I didn't write it,' she says. She'll grin at the silent room, hook back a strap of hair. Or look down into her glass, fingernails of thin ice drifting inside.

Tinfoil, bandage. Eve adds them to the shiny line across the quilt. Down in the base of the kit she finds the fold of material, peels the corner up and pulls at it. Out of the flare of orange hanky the purse mirror spins. The mirror is a palm-sized circle of plastic, pinched from the makeup-junk her mother has stashed with pills in a shoebox under the bed. It still smells of powder and lashgrease, the blue-tinged juice that congeals at her mother's lids. Shadows of window and skin fall through the mirror.

When Eve has it flat in her hand she holds its reflection up to the ceiling, moving it forward carefully. As if it could spill.

*

Tonight Eve's sitting her Rescuer's Badge, so Tui has had to call Brown Owl in. Most of the other girls are doing their Hostess or Toymaker, so Tui is busy testing the etiquette of tea-parties, the feather-stitch on sets of dolls' underclothes. Politely she has tried to draw Eve towards Country Dancer or Child Nurse. But the girl has stuck to the sweaty dramas which Brown Owl encourages, of gorse on fire and rolling tractors. Walking a bearing of X to a dark tree, sliding her fingers over grid references, freezing in stalking postures, making smoke-prints — all things which Tui can't test. Tui's developed a new kind of sigh for it, a chin-down high-breasted sigh, like balloons of sour air are slowly inflating under her ribs.

When Eve has chanted over her six tips on What To Do If You're Lost In The Bush, and shown on a child's fake telephone How To Dial Police and Fire Brigade, Brown Owl takes her outside to the curve of black gravel around Takewhero hall. Before she walks the eleven metres from Eve, Brown Owl pulls her socks up, and pats the girl on the back with a meaty hand. Eve looks down at the fuzz of cold hair on the bulge above Brown Owl's sock-tops, the glossy disc of the watch belted sturdily over her wrist.

'Ready for me to plunge into danger?' the woman says. A shake in the child's chin, in the wet lip. 'I've never been so jolly confident of a rescue, you know, cadet.' Eve watches the weathered sac beneath the round eyes crumple. She feels her face prickle with warm blood.

As she stands watching Brown Owl's clumpy retreat she remembers the handbook diagrams, and checks the rope coil. Holding hand one-third, throwing hand two. She feels her nose running and pulls up her throwing hand, strawish bristles scratching her lip and chin. The rope smells like farmdust and nuts in their wrinkled coffins.

When the call comes from the faraway smudge of Brown Owl she jets out her throwing hand, shouting. The noise uncurls in the darkening air with the falling rope like smoke.

*

She puts the mirror as close to her mother's mouth as she can without having to touch. As she waits for the tiny circle to fog she closes her own throat. She feels the stick-shape of her ribcage like a splint. When finally her mother's breath coats the mirror, she thinks the wet pattern moves in and out with her thoughts. *Without having to touch. Without having to touch.*

*

Once, twice. Nowhere near her. The third time it falls short her recoiling slows. She feels the burn of fibres round her elbow spread like threads to her face. The rustle of stones at her shoes like thin black seeds. And when she looks back up Brown Owl is standing a body-length closer.

'I realised I miscounted,' Brown Owl chortles. 'Stupid old chook, eh? Keep it going. Four times under a minute twenty. That's all we need.'

This time the line hits her well in the stocky knees. 'Well done girl!' her voice booms forward. She bounds up, looking past the glaze on the girl's face. 'Chop, chop. It's time for the bowline.'

Back inside Eve rubs at her eyes. Brown Owl steers her firmly past the sewing groups. An under-breath giggle of 'It's B.O' lifts after them, but Brown Owl does not stop. Tui's head doesn't turn, as she stands in an elegant ring of cross legs, one white finger modelling a glinting silver thimble.

They go to a corner and Brown Owl stands her facing the wall. 'Ignore all the others. Bowline. In your own time.'

Eve passes the rope around her waist and stands with it in outstretched hands, looking down at the high-polished floor where the big hall deepens like a sea-bottom. Drifting in the floor she sees the tall yellow streak of windows, blue Guide bodies hung with apron, dolls' clothes stretched with light. She tries to keep the black loops of the handbook diagram in her mind, the bowline tied by hands cut off at the wrists. She tries to walk her fingers through their web of lettered circles, to remember the three steps, *W, A & S*. She's fed the rope round her body for days now, looping and hauling herself in her bedroom, poised with a kind of love as she feels the line about to be pulled tight. She pictures the images: on the page, the rope looks like it floats on water, and in its biggest pool she sees the tiny subset labelled 'body'. *The bowline*, Eve remembers, *is the most useful knot for rescue purposes. A bowline may be tied with one hand, and if tied correctly, it will not slip.* Not like a noose, Eve knows from her mother. Her mother's knots always give.

THE DAY THAT YOU CRASH your car will be the loudest of your life. You're a teenage girl and you think the car that you're driving is as solid as a moving room: like your bedroom at home with tapes of the Doors and Eagles and ten-cent pieces in dust and a novel which opens itself at the dirty bits and chewing gum and even a stash of tampons in the glove box . . . then all that is crushed to a bloom of iron and glass and your skin is the vase for it.

That's a sound, for sure, but it's not just that. It's the second you see it coming that's louder, or even the second before. And in one sense you don't see it coming at all, because your eye gets it so *wrong*: whatever is shining up from the road and rain and sky into your eye isn't really the way things *are*. Not the black stones in the wet curve or the white line that breaks up along it, not the needles of rain that rise in the light. Your eye thinks it knows everything, it's got a graph of things: glare, water, trees, turn, space. But then, it's as if some-one jars the film, there's a jump-cut to some other scene entirely. There's another place where the road smooths out in a curve into town, a loose left-hander you could sleep through it's such a wheel of slow and cool, and then a long right swerve to slip out the backstreets to high school. That's when another road suddenly slides from your eye and a dark car cuts through your pupil, and as soon as your eye is fixed on that your gut gets a jump-cut too. You can't pull out of the turn now — that's when the sound starts to gather itself. It mixes itself from the throb of the last trees past you, the gash of stones on the road and the gas-pedal's pump, because of course you *speed up*, hoping you might get past it. After all, your eye might have it wrong.

You think you might make it, until you hear Max in the back seat saying, *holy shit*. It's funny that those words coming from him, who doesn't believe in Bibles or prayers or Judas or even sin, should sound like the word of God. Like God just looks down and says, *shit no, you're not gonna make it*. But that's when you know for sure, holy shit.

The other two people in the car don't say anything. You remember their later sounds though, curdled words, throat-broken. By then, you know you could edge out from under the wheel, say, *My Dad owns this town*, stalk off. Afterwards they all treat you like you do. But you don't. You listen to them, you watch what they are trying to say coming up through blood. You never leave them.

You watch the woman you hit too, and she makes no sound, because she's worse. They put you in the ambulance, and you can see them cutting her out from there, sawing and peeling the car from her slowly like it's a chrysalis.

But that comes later, after the car you're in suddenly climbs a staircase, steps of tree, clay, windshield, jaw. And once your car has crawled over hers, it spins. It's hard to describe that spin. It's like all you learnt in science class, all those laws that keep your feet in the dirt, the sky around your brain, the sea where it should be, all those laws are lost for an instant. The river of nerves in your body feels them reversing. Your body suddenly lets light through, opens to all the knowledge of spinning, so every cell of you feels the mass and axis and force of the earth. Your car's buzzing off it like a moth off a light bulb.

Max is the one who leaves. He is the one. As soon as you stop he gets out. You, Elaine, Jess: none of you remember him being there when you come round, though he's the first person each of you call for. You're all in love with him. That sounds stupid, but it has to be said. Jess has been in the passenger seat and she's slid forward to hit the dashboard. She's wearing a mouth of jelly when you look over at her, but you still hear his name, the muscles in her neck slowly making it. Elaine has been behind your back, her knees up on your seat. She's been swotting for calculus, the exam you're all on your way to today, but she hasn't seen the real-life equation coming, has she? The angle of two dark cars multiplied by the rain.

Less the circumference of your heart, perhaps.

And this is where the equation gets tricky, because of what you've seen in your rear view mirror, just before you crash. You've seen Max, moving into her. His fingers grazing her leg beneath her textbook, his breath working into her ear. She's woken up, foetal-shape, stuffed down in the footspace behind the driver seat, and when she's pulled out you can see, from the glow of slashes above her collar, that the textbook has left her a pattern of paper-cuts to last a lifetime. She hasn't let it go, and on either side of its thick spine she's snapped fingers, although it's cushioned her face, which only seems to shine more with the red necklace under it.

You figure Max will choose her.

Yet he doesn't stay with any of you at first. You catch sight of him from the ambulance. He's standing out in the crowd, as if he's just been passing by and paused to watch the cars, a drifter, like his favourite song, a loner, desperado. When the officer comes to the back of the ambulance to ask questions you point over to Max, but he's moved already. By now the woman has been carved out of her wreck and put in the ambulance with you, and it's too late to answer anything. You choke to look at her.

What's under the long dark hair is what's under every face. But it still hits you to see it, the things that do your kissing, chewing, answering.

You don't see Max again, until x-ray. He suddenly appears as you're waiting, sitting by the picture of the *Mona Lisa* who has a cut-out fringe of lighted teeth along her jaw. There's another painting like this, further down the corridor, a big lush nude, of the kind your father would howl about on school or

calculus   147

church committees, with a section of x-rayed ribs that look like hair haloed in rain. You're by yourself; Jess and Elaine are having themselves wired up with stitches, bandages, tubes, a kind of metal cage going over Elaine's hands. Her fingers have been pushed back into place; you've kept your hand on her forehead during that. She hasn't looked you in the eyes, she's looked like she does when she's staring up at something on the blackboard, a formula with too many bits of the alphabet for anyone to see. But Elaine's mind can branch around anything. You just have to know what to start with, she tells you, and then their relationship to each other. Find that first value and you can pull the problem open like a knot.

But you're something her eyes don't see. An ugly, loving variable.

Seeing that picture of bones beneath the woman's chest has made you feel kind of sick by the time Max turns up in x-ray. Whatever's under your chest is not translucent, like a sketch of angel. You've started to hear a sticky sound when you breathe. When Max comes in he touches you on your arm and there's a splicing of heat that sends roots running down into your stomach and winding as far as your forehead. You ask him if he knows about the woman you hit, and he says maybe she's going to be driven on to the city unit. He makes his fingers into a church of triangles and you stare through them, lino through bones. 'She's had it, if you ask me.'

When it's your turn, he helps you undress for the pictures and get into the white gown. They shut you in a cubicle and he doesn't look at your face while he takes off your clothes. You can't believe he's this close to you, beneath your dress, your hooks and buttons. You think, if your father comes in now he'll have a fit. But you know, as you feel every hair on your arms, every pore on your breasts shift and open for him, you know he isn't interested in you. The radiographer comes to get you, they flatten you out like an abacus: the whole time you shake there thinking of Max in the cubicle, of how he leans his head into you. You see him coming, slow, magnetic, the trajectory of a kiss, and he mutters, 'It was your fault. Don't you let Daddy cover for you. It was your fault. Hear me?'

When you come out from the x-ray he's waiting to walk you back down the hall. He leads you into the accident room where Elaine and Jess are still being seen to, and you're supposed to wait while they read your results. There's a woman from education who's trying to make Elaine hold a pen: she has to sit the exam if she wants to keep her scholarship. They've taken the metal cage off her right hand, but she can't close the fingers. Her whole arm jerks with trying to get the mangled sticks to make a claw. It's no good. 'Try the left hand,' the woman says. 'We'll give you extra time. You just have to sit it.' The nurse unravels some straps, and the woman tries poking the pen through. It sticks between two swollen knuckles, and the woman slips her pad beneath it. Two big cords stand out under Elaine's ear. Each hand is a black fork.

'This is fuckin' ridiculous,' Max says. He tries to throw the pen out into the corridor. It hits the legs of the traffic officer who's coming in to ask you more questions. But what you remember is watching how gently Max leans in to settle Elaine. Her eyes aren't wet, but the lids around them twitch, look raw. She's marginal, marked out in your small town; there are rumours about her family, warnings. Without her scholarship she knows she'll never make it: if she wasn't Miss Genius she wouldn't have been allowed in the car with you. Max's mouth is pale, defined against her sequence of scratches.

Then your father walks in.

'Your princess caused it,' Max says.

You think of how you open your eyes after blacking out somewhere in the car's circles, and imagine his body spat into gravel, a piece of holy graffiti. There will never be enough white crosses; you will make it a shrine.

There is such piety in his face. He repeats, 'She's to blame. Little princess.'

Your father regards him. 'Quite the crusader, aren't you. Quite the hero.'

Elaine cries out something. Your father turns to her, pointing, firm. 'That injury, young lady, was entirely preventable. If you'd been wearing your seat belt, as you should have been, it would never have occurred.'

You hear him and feel like you've crashed through the steel instrument tray at the bedside.

'It wouldn't have happened if your daughter hadn't totalled the car,' Max says. 'She knows it. She'll tell you so.' He looks at you.

His look is a dissection.

You know now, this is your chance. You have to repeat what Max has told you. You haven't seen anything, or what you've seen you haven't made sense of, but he has. He's *told* you what you've seen. He's told you the truth.

You would say it instantly, if you thought he'd stand by you.

The doctor walks in, the dark square of your damage under his arm.

He lights you up on the white board, but you already feel transparent. There is the skinny crooked you. There's your anatomy: shadows, talons. Longing has split through the muscles around your heart.

You'll always believe you manage to whisper *it was my fault*, but no one hears it. Your father extends his hand toward the officer; his voice is suave, precise. The officer puts a hand on Max's collarbone, but your father motions, benign. Your father, the officer, the doctor move to a corner, behind a screen. You hear their voices, monotone, fluent with local knowledge, small-town concern. The woman's family works for your father; arrangements can be informally made. Her car is not registered, has no warrant, but booze and speed are well documented.

They come back around the curtain, pragmatic, composed. You say, 'But her face, her face . . .'

You look at your father's face. The trenches around his nose are lit up with sweat. You see the yellow roots of his teeth as he smiles, his tongue's thick underside.

'You're distraught,' he says. 'Understandably. You'll have to lie down. You should have been seen to.'

But while he tells you to lie down, you're already falling.

The fall takes place at many angles. Faces enter it, expand, withdraw. But the end of the fall is distinct: Jess bends by your head, putting down some paper. It's the education woman's paper, her pen; Jess has retrieved them, bland, methodical Jess, movements you have not seen. But you see the track of her small note, although you don't know who it is written to. It's measured and tidy in one corner, a secret triangle, ready to be severed from the page. The lines are darker than those across her mouth: *Should I be telling them about our baby?*

So this is where the sound gathers again, but you're almost relieved by now. Max is wiping your mouth with a bandage which is also an inside-out rose. Elaine is somewhere close to you reading a shattered silver book, but you can't make out her longitude because your eye has slid open at speed. It can no longer knit the lines of the room you're in to its moving surface. The people that work above you come in loud pulses of tree and glass, but your eye isn't to blame. You try to tell them it's not to blame, but the muscle under your face can shape nothing. Another woman is crying in there and you offer her a beer, some keys. The sound of your heart, its dark lines pulling the wheel, begins to worry you, but they're seeing to its ugliness now, they've realised it's the first value. Over the woman's chin are ferns of shadow, and while she sings the tattoo swims. You look into the spirals of black oil and the exam begins.

X. MILKDANCE: LINDA'S DIARY

11 thursday
My hair grew long again — in dreams, last night. Long,
oiled, and my spine knew it. How does it happen so simply in
dreams? You're utterly inside your skin, its tensions, but at the
same time you look on at yourself, rib, lip, broken detail. And
there was my hair, the length of it, remembered down my
spine, chilly. It poured through my scalp as smoothly as blood
looping through a vein.

Not much to write of, the pressure of that paleness.
And *hair* — I'd never choose that fibre as any kind of symbol.
Too feathery for grief, the way a princess would define a loss.
But the moment I woke, these two thoughts opened, cleared,
in my mind. I felt them in the membrane. They were not there
as a chain, one idea linking, or branching, into another. They
were somehow there at once, each within the other, like circles
in water disturbed. I thought of having Sally curled at the teat,
taking milk from me. The ends of my unwashed hair had
worked down over my breast and she'd sucked a strip into her
mouth. When I tried to slide it out, I drew out lengths, like
fishline. I remember worrying how far into her throat it had
spread. Tired, guilty girl-mother I was then I kept on shivering,
filled with fear at this hairy ribbon, crisp with knots, and milk
matted. And I thought of the worst dream Sally herself, as a
little girl, had woken from: there'd been a frog on a pedestal,
she'd told me, green as the storybook, poised to be kissed.
Instead she had watched herself bend down and take a dark
bite out of it.

So I woke up bald. My spine knows baldness now, as well
as it ever knew hair — the bony egg-shaped bloom of my skull
from its tip. A thin bulb, cool, mottled. Sally is soon coming

milkdance: linda's diary

home. This time, quietly, she has threatened to bring her girlfriend with her.

14 sunday

Jack: I watched him, alone with the dishes tonight, after he'd put me in the chair, insisted. Tucked in the blanket around my legs, his fingers orderly, cupped (for no reason at all this crocheted web of old wool smells like my grandmother). Under the orange kitchen lamp he worked, the sink lapping and clinking, and it was the sound of courtship I heard as I let my eyelids close the day down. Old plates afloat in the cooling sink, oil ringing the steel — this space in our days was a time of murmurs, of approaching touch. Measures of gentleness we made amongst this most banal of chores — a pause of fingers along the damp band of an apron, a brush of foam from the wrist. And he is still tender in his routine, although we no longer have little pieces of gossip to trade, anecdotes of the baby or the office, falls from the trees, broken toys, parking tickets. Instead he puts on some music, sometimes shuffles his slippers on the lino, grinning at me, winking, spry.

When he thinks I've drifted off, the dancing halts. I hear the sigh he holds in, against the lung, I hear the compression. It's the act of folding the tea-towel that stops that contraction. That's all it is. The tenderness of monotony, that links him back to the pattern of our ordinary days.

15 monday

First married, we had a red couch, broken, cat-clawed. Each winter we had to lure out a nest of mice. But what I've been remembering are the days when I lay under Jack on it, jaw calling for spasm, spine rubbing the pitted velvet.

We'd aged, even before the sickness. The sex had become slack, muted. There was the same familiar fitting together, hip and breast to fingers' cup. But tiredness lined each touch.

So . . . perhaps it was not before my illness.

16 tuesday
I've said I want the girlfriend to come, but I know he's not repeating this.

I want her to come. I've heard her in the background some days when I've spoken to Sally — a certainty, a bulk, jarring, blunt. Jack hums to me, pauses, as if a vibration will sink my body — I want someone to talk to me as if my bones will survive their voice.

Like that shriek — next door, the little girl, naked, in gumboots, white plastic wings. She throws pine-needles, howls at her brother, whose games always crush her: *make it I can't die today.*

18 thursday
I must think to tell Sally of that earlier piece: how tender her father is. The last time she was here, they wheeled me out for a garden breakfast — we watched, through the cutting, the man who lives next door stringing lines of washing out. Child things, structureless, still half-dirty, limp with sadness — he hung them up with such awkwardness, muscle flickered in his face. Only weeks before his wife had left him — but it was the days of my treatment. Lists of the gestures, offers I would have made, evaporated then: I should have bottled from their spilling trees, frozen meals, given the children haircuts. When I'm well I'm that type of woman: I believe in networks, in sweetness — when you are alone with children, such small acts can be all that holds up your day. But that morning, with Sally there, watching him hang out his children's clothes was . . . something so *moving* my breathing trembled the scar, seemed to dislodge stitches. Then Jack looked over, shrugged

back at Sally and me, and muttered with precision: 'No doubt his wife left him because he's gay then.'

There's scaffolding to build before I go, reinforcement. But sweetness, network, takes tissue, takes bone — elements I'm short of.

19 friday

Last night, on our television, women began their lovemaking. Jack removed the image — lace on a desk, wrist buckling, wet pores under a tongue — but not before I'd seen his face.

He left the room. But I sat thinking how unaltered this scene was from any other, where it was a man who pressed a woman, rode and opened nipples, lips. The women were both gaunt, entrepreneurial. They dug under business suits, silk in office tones. Their greasy mouths echoed in glass, their lingerie slipped across documents.

I sat thinking: this isn't how I imagined it.

I have tried to imagine the ways another woman might touch my daughter. Illness has made me think of it more — I don't know why that is.

Yes, I do — my body no longer talks of convention. It's started to speak of death. I'm outside that circle of disgust that Jack decided for us. I don't think I ever shared it. I close my eyes, and simply see her touched with love, anonymous, open — the flesh beneath the tenderness speaking of life, rippling with it.

21 sunday

Reading back about Jack — it was a dance, our first date. Jack and I, in a high-school hall, music threshing through tinny speakers, dry ice piped across gooseflesh and frill. Long black seams of sex up our calves, the stiletto's erotic fragility, and that year all of the girls craved meatless bodies, the horny wing of the collarbone. Around our mouths a cheesy tint sweated into makeup; eyelids, puffy and fluttering, were a toilet-cleaner blue. Jack and I stupidly tried to kiss as we staggered against each other, jazz choking itself from the drunk school band. It came out not so much a kiss as a kind of worming around of lips. Jack's tongue, back then, tended to strain at its blue leash, to fight its own slippery muscle, and it was months before I could bear to say. Besides, I felt the flex of my throat, nerves of vodka splintering in it. I burrowed into the plastic shine of his hire tux — nothing would ever be perfect. Already I'd spent the day in terror — acne bubbled up from my chin, a red core, burning, topped with a greenish crust. I was terrified it would break, throb and run if he knocked it, kissing me — twice as I'd greased it over, orange concealer so thick it held fingerprints, it had opened, oozed out into the paint.

I'd wept as if it was a tumour. I'd stared at myself in the bathroom mirror, ribs under blue silk, hive of glittering hair, and eyelids glowing, fatty with pain. Such teenage pain. Arcs of smooth, powdered skin — but I did not see them, I only saw the one raw mutation. I thought my body had betrayed me in the worst way.

24 wednesday
I went to bed and I dreamt of Andrea. Sally's bringing her to meet me soon. I've never seen her, not even in photos, yet I knew it was her bending over my dream. She leant down, a kind of grace, of observance, ran her tongue over my scar's angle. My dead breast burned, unlaced itself from its jagged strings, and grew again.

XI. THIS LINGUISTIC SKIN

magnificat falling

1.
still yourself
but also another

holding life in
broken waters

2.
you split & quicken
quilt & misalign me

signal yourself in
the opaque language

of pain

3.
swim
the beating silence

of your home
against the bone

4.
tonight I feel you
rustling fluids &
moving the intimate
boundaries of me

you understand doubleness:
for you breathing
is drowning

5.
hostess
  enclosure

sweet
parasite

6.
the sky gulls softly
a lullaby over
a swollen woman

spreading her red self:
skull of a wrinkled sun

7.
struggles with scarlet:
yet she is a little in
love with her own ruin

footnote in irises;
ibid, in blood

8.
you lie
limbing me idly

your dull syllabic
thud the mothering
of my tongue

9.
magnificat

                    falling

10.
milk-sweat
of an ambivalent breast:

already love
lets down

11.
sending down soft
probes of sound

you remember yourself
in black transparency

skeletal thumbelina
vertebrate doll

12.
wetness assembles
a thick shine
rimming

a life a lip an eye

13.
Opening day
waiting for pain
to pull you inside out

Alice grown fat
in the land
of falling

14.
palpating braille

we speak each other

cell mates
through sinuous wall

gravida, gravida

*

today the child inside
me makes me sicker than I've
ever been, I shake
out the yellow bodies before
I hang up their bloodless
clothes. the day is in
the key of summer
the violet sky is highly
strung & my son
asks me *how do you*
open water?

*

into the stainless evening
I'm pouring

the blood
off the family meat

*

They say the dark womb wanders
like a stranger with a sad song in its mouth

scarlet unregenerate
it displays its rich black tongue

or drags its longing out
through border towns

the fibres of its shrunken gown
are shimmers in the hot throat of the mind

*

morning has broken
again & again

the first bird's bones
are feathers & splinters

*

my son's voice
from another room

he's days beyond
my looking after

he asks why I'm
still in bed

*doesn't she know
which way day is?*

*

Beneath my fingers
you're still

only a shadow
of a doubt

What have I fed you on?

gravida, gravida   169

a heart of salt
a fringe of bones

*

if this were a garden
I would lower

myself to the soil
the darkness sunk into water

around me shining
& overexposed

my cold face spined & open
like a bright meat-eating flower

fresh from the word

*

all day in the kitchen she asks
herself, how can I make
a poem from this? I'm an old
old woman & my shoes are red
with bony song. my fingers are ringed
like onion skins dirt-mooned & willing
the knife to nothing inside

*

you & I
alone in this body

sit in the mess
of its dawn

this week they say
your heart is forming

it's in my mouth
my strangled babe

*

All afternoon as I try
to sleep, you scrabble away
inside me — a possum at the end
wall of a dark room of an empty house.
I imagine your wet eyes ringed with light.

dressing Orestes

we were not immaculate
for love is attended by blood

water dried in your hair
& milk on your mouth

nevertheless we dressed you in white
& gowned like a ghost you left my body

a small levitation of grief
clean in another's arms

small pieces

*

after
the baby her body
is thinned
but
looser like
a dress (or a dream)
cut out
for an older
sister

or
a sister
sewn
for an older
dream

*

you are so
tired
that when you close
your eyes

they sink like stones into water

roll back
like the only
moving part

of the doll you
had as
a child

playtime

if I could believe in the town it might stay up another day & let the park love the children moving & putting their mouths on the metal bars & mothers like myself who call stay down from there & moving bottles left by the drunks & the children learning to be drunk & the heavy bodies of the trees wearing their name tags telling us we never learnt latin & the bark brought home on the children to a line of brown water around the bath which you wash away with the same movement each night as the water looks through the hole the same way & sings to another town wet-eyed where the women wear faces named after trees & the children climb them always drinking the language of bodies of brown & latin water & the town has set aside a day to wash them & build them see-saws which turn love over their knees they knit with white bread & belief

1.
butterflies today

salt water,
fingernails

apples & learning to
kiss

2.
summer days the baby splashes in language fingering its wet suffix on
his skin says 'wet' & 'water' as if the sounds connect his self to the
memory & to my body wet with the touch of his which whispers 'yes,
water' knowing as soon as the sound is made the water slips away

3.
My son is painting
his first pictures, I
am tidying away. My
question is this: when do we
stop making memories
and start making
detritus?

worse still
sentiment,
I hear them
say.

4.
after the morning has finished talking
we take its photograph. The baby sits in the wet grass
thinking a lemon is a yellow ball. The door to the old shed
has let itself go, so you must break it open with your body. The wood
feeds itself to the spiders inside. I have become the kind of woman who
does the washing the night before & sometimes hangs it out in the
darkness. It is still there this morning, wet, evidential

5.
back lawn stretching its new word 'green' & lazy, your face a
miracle of mischief bringing me sun screened fistfuls of thin stalks
serious delicacies crush & thread & test the buttery mysteries of skin
but cannot say daisy chains, say 'chasey days'

6.
today the poems cannot go outside
press their faces to the window like children
always watch you leave

7.
you are now learning the language of your body
before your body has a language of its own

jump you scream when your feet are grounded
skip which the grammar of your legs can't prove
fast which is how you came to this place
where your mind mouths images you can't move

8.
washing the heart out with soap we know

HER BODY RISES

there's trouble in every fairytale
how else do we recognise poison and glass

9.
putting on clothes from the day before shaped with the memory smell of
your body with places where secrets have left their hands your heaviness
a dream of others the language of marigold egg & lipstick thickness
of fingers mirroring mouths all to be eaten with the resolve of a child's
first kiss of seeing itself in the sleepless love of a mother face before you
clean & divide it in a sign

10.
you are an angel of play & orange juice
blocks & the musical pulp of fruit
a whole day's sun waste on the floor

11.
mother's veins
must surely be rivers

change course
flood

words you pick up today: blood, stones
words I find today: monody, gravid

12.
here is the skin of nostalgia reading you books in a single bed
your listening mouth wet head hot soft bowl & singing answers to
how I wonder what you are an alphabet of bones an intertissuing
your eye folding the slowness of holding sleep slip fingered a noon

Diary for Liam

for storyless children are living syllables intrinsic his bread left love
sucked on the nightstand palate roses nappies rolled into their
warm blooms on the floor

13.
these are my days
& I'm at home in them

My children colour me in.

I have a blue arm, skinny as a vein.

One eye, a *ladybird, ladybird,* legs like hair sucked onto the page.

For a fringe they've picked off a wing.

Pink-lips, drink-lips, in-the-sink-lips.

The other eye rides *up to the bone where your hair ends.*

There it glints like a detonator.

Over my head a snotty mat of stars.

Red-teeth, fed-teeth, get-into-bed-teeth.

Spit on their knuckles they circle my belly of wax

& stretch a necklace through it.

Later there'll be animals stuck in a gluey flood

because the man from the Bible didn't get

the sea cut open for you in time.

Brown-hand, down-hand, watch-me-drown-hand.

They wash my hair in a scribble of fire, freckle

my cheek with breadcrumb kisses.

In between my legs they make a fist of glitter *that we grew in.*

I point to the peach sack left beside me.

That's where you jumped out of your skin.

*

My son picks up
the book I'm reading.
It is *A Body of Water*.
Looking for pictures,
he finds none.
A book about letters, he says.

*

Six months on
he brings me a book
of short stories.
What's this about? I say.
About the man's mountain
& swimming in red water,
my son says.
About swimming under
the mountain, the men
in big red water.

*

Warm-limbed in late
afternoon, he slides
up under *Angels & Insects*,
the sound of hair & skin
push past the page
into my lap. He makes
himself an obstacle of love
& kicks the book shut.

Mummy, his small breath
says against my neck,
I'm tired of words.

HER BODY RISES

DOWN IN THE KNUCKLES OF the grass lived a fly that was eating the face of Chloe's pet lamb. Chloe's father had told her the cause, and told her not to play with Cinders, but then he had gone and now she couldn't remember much of what he said. Before he left he had fenced a patch off in the back yard against the old house, and now when Chloe climbs up for dinner she's told not to look at the lamb out the window, its slippery bunting mouth on the plastic fence, its poodle-tail not flapping but limp with drying tendrils of shit. In and out, as she slips the fat from her chops, as she punctures peas on her fork prongs, the slack bleat of the lamb keeps coming through her mother's nets. The sound shivers, and makes her think of the hot pleats of the lamb's mouth, pushing slimily over her fingertips.

Chloe keeps laying four sets of knives and forks at the table. She does it without thinking, yanking open the gritty drawer, loading each hand with cold weight. She rolls each ropey place mat out with its sticky nodes of yolk or sauce, freckles as personal as the face or the fingerprint that dropped them.

Tonight is the sixth night she's made the mistake. Her mother doesn't bend her head but lets her left eye drizzle water onto the skinny willow of her plate. The children watch it coming to nest against the blue-brown bone. Chloe's brother Michael picks up the useless fork and stabs at her eyeline. Chloe stares at the four metal stars until her eye makes darker strings and the fork looks like a power pole, dissected by voices and birds in the buzzing distance.

The old house, which smells like moths, is behind the new one, which still smells like pink batts. The old house was supposed to be pushed down, but first her father was going to strip it of things like the grills on the fireplace, the doorknobs which are curly gold flowers and the wiry tiles of glass that pock your face with colour as you move past. Chloe is not supposed to play in the old house because of the floorboards. But now Chloe's father won't know, and besides she likes the feel of the fibres splitting as she skips through the house. It's just like the noise of her milk-teeth when her father tied a brick to the loosest, the long roots making one last snap before they lifted out a tangle of blood.

When they first moved to the farm there were so many things that a little girl dreamed of. Her mother hadn't wanted to come, but Chloe had run round for days. She'd dragged a picnic into the dark jagged church beneath the honeysuckle, she'd slouched off her boots and pointed her blue toes in the wormy grass of the creek. She'd jumped from fence posts with her raincoat like a cape and her red palm a star of splinters. At the highest point of the farm she'd picked up coils of furry shit and twirled them off the clay lip like a discus.

The most amazing thing had been a swarm of miniature ponies, pale dwarf horses that rushed and jittered loose around the fields. The drunk old man who'd sunk the farm had driven them to the shore in summer and propped hot kids on their bulging ribs for rides along the beach. But long before his blue heart finally clapped out in the old house, he'd given up on the brutes and let them prowl lazily through the wires, clop up the steps and sink their horny teeth in the verandah trim. Sometimes Chloe found tufted hives of shit dropped in the old house, but when she tried to lure the ponies back in they stood staring, scrunching. Chloe spent hours stalking with string, daydreamed of plaits with oily ribbon, but she never got close enough to touch them, to pick off their patchwork coats of crap or brush out the crusts that ran down their tails like seaweed. She never came home with anything but a catch of fat silky flowers, the heads of dahlias wrangled and sweating in her noose.

Then her father had knocked in wires, planted pumpkins and windbreak trees that looked like a line of broken hands. The ponies had been rounded up and one of them had bucked and opened a velvet artery down the ramp of the truck. So Chloe continues to stake out the old house, to cook in the possum-shit of the old stove, to crouch and stare at the holes in the floor. Days when she's very angry she's even brave enough to poke down an arm, sliding her body up to the hole until her fingers hit dirt. The best days she's dug up blue-glass bottles, spoons with cabbagey silver ends, and even a little jewellery box that had opened its hinge with a cough and let out a ring of something crumbly that might once have been hair.

She pictures the fly, its wings with a pattern like fog-veins on the window, the sticky hair growing jaggedly down its six legs. Once, when her father had been away, he'd sent Chloe a post-card, a view of a lamb that was sugar-white in a clumpy paddock of daffodils. An orange butterfly balanced on its ear like the plastic numbered tags her father sometimes shot in the animals' heads.

But Cinders had not been white. And she had been *hers*, only hers. Chloe had watched her born: a wet dark handbag of bones that elbowed out of the ewe's rippling body. Chloe had known from that first slosh that Cinders was a magical lamb. She was so black that when Chloe pushed her hands along the lamb's thick loops she imagined her skeleton under the fleece, a lacework of greasy black bones.

But Chloe's lamb had been greedy. She'd chewed down deep, deeper, angrier into the pasture than lambs should know how to go. Past the yellow roots, the dirty juice, down into her father's land. Her nipping, rustling teeth had woken the fly. Chloe's father said not to touch her. But after school no one is home now, her father has left, her mother is working, and has to trust Chloe and Michael to look after themselves. So Chloe has still been sliding into the pen and brushing the scaly face, tracing the pale patches of crust that are speckled from the fly. The fly has sucked Cinders' colour away until now she's the shade of the skin that flaps on the top of Chloe's goodnight Milo, left to cool before bedtime.

From Chloe's bed the phone sounds like the sheets of corrugated iron she remembers flagging from the roof of the old house. She remembers her father, days or years ago in the distance, starting the work, poised on the soft joists, pulling back the rusted drains like flax. The unanswered phone makes Chloe think of the dark strokes of his crowbar, the welt of sound as his pale arm bucked.

Her mother never answers the phone now, because of the night of dirty calls. Chloe had seen her mother that night, holding the mouthpiece away from her body as if she had touched the electric fence. There had been tendons as thick as drill bits standing above her collarbone. Then two nights later they heard voices, jokes on the porch, knuckles popping on the walls, cigarettes flicking past splits in the curtains. Once, the bump on the wall was so hard the plastic curtain rail shifted, the slippery hooks running sideways to open a wider piece of moon. Her mother made them ball up, hidden, smaller beside the bed. The voices kept talking of dark places, targets on her mother's body — now the man of the house was gone, they said. As half-light began, the voices left and Chloe watched her mother's skin. A frieze of sweat darkened the fish lines that crimped across her stomach.

Her mother had said to ignore the nights of ringing, stay in her bed. She'd said it's just like the game they used to play in their city-house, the one where the mothers in the street would ring around warning 'God-squad's here!'. 'Just like playing possum,' she'd explained, a finger on Chloe's lips, even making a skimpy fist at Michael when he argued with her. 'Remember the God-squad,' she kept saying, trying to joke the memories out: the women would phone the alert round and Chloe's mother would grab the kids and sprint to the kitchen, giggling down behind the bench. Her lips would make a laughing 'shush' as the men tapped politely on all the doors and once even padded behind the house calling out 'Anyone in?' in holy but disappointed voices. The mothers used to get together for coffee when the all-clear had gone, and laugh at the squeaky-shoed Mormons, roaming whole streets where no one was ever at home.

Chloe tries to pull the memory into sleep with her. On the funniest day, she remembers, they hadn't heard the phone. Her mother had settled down to bake topless. Chloe had watched her dark flesh. She liked to study the wide brown nipples oiled and loose in the sunshine, the ring of stretchmarks swimming up the wonky base of her boob like fish.

Chloe thinks of her mother's gasp as the men arrived holding their zip-up Bibles. Big sunglasses and bigger breasts seemed to gape at the tidy men, then Chloe's mother pulled her shrieking, in through the ranchslider, down to their normal hunch beneath the sink. Chloe had watched her mother's giggle grating her boob up and down on her ribs, the goose-flesh nipple in its glitter of hairs changing into a fingertip.

She tries to keep the image in her mind to fight the ringing. She can almost sleep if she pictures the warm strings in her mother's breast, the scaly lino in their city-house, the smell and colour of weetbix. But the phone sounds like her father, wings of pale muscle working, the darkest spines of the old house peeling, beating toward the ground.

Chloe has found a dictionary left behind in the old house. It isn't buried under the floor but pushed into the meat safe. A light pattern of mesh is baked in the cloth that wraps it. When she shucks it, a pollination of dense orange dust.

She looks for the fly. The letter F is a fingerprint cut in the book's gold edge. But nothing listed has quite the sense of her fly, of what her Dad said. Pictures of her fly are there, the jaws, the rope of milky eggs. But tilting her finger up through the yellow column she gets *flyleaf*: 'a blank page,' it says. She understands nothing until she gets to the darker head of the column. The hieroglyphics shift around in the brackets, themselves like tiny wings and legs: 'To depart swiftly; to run away; to flee; to be fugitive; to become diffused or spread rapidly; to burst in pieces . . .'

After the night of the voices, Chloe hovers, watching her mother. She stands behind her, close, in the narrow doorway as her mother cuts her hair. The scissors are old but her mother stands patiently wetting and sawing off pellets. They flop to the lino like clots that Chloe remembers in the pony's blood. Chloe watches until it's finished, letting the last grit wash her face, land, and stick like tinsel in the frills of her dress.

Her mother says nothing when Chloe picks up the darker tails, slipping them into a plastic bag like eels.

In the old house she finds her brother, smoking. Michael doesn't normally come here, but today he's propped against the brick, pale smoke roping his face, banging the fag on a hip-bone shape of plate that Chloe's pulled out of the pit.

'Littered with ghosts, this bloody place.'

Chloe lays beside the hole, letting her head sink into the plastic. The bag sighs, the hair nesting under her skull.

'What you got there?'

'Mum. It's her hair. Cut off.'

He doesn't say anything. Chloe hears the hard skin of his thumb chinking the lighter wheel. More smoke puffs in the cut-glass dusk of the room and she watches her right arm rolling, drooping into the hole. Fibres pull in the floorboards' rind.

'You'll fuckin' fall in, you silly cow.'

'I don't care.'

'Well. Mum does.'

She brushes three of her fingernails along, feels the gristly soil building. A flicker of something denser is telegraphed from wrist to rib, the prickle of elements waiting to break the skin, wanting skin to be buried with them.

'You think they'll come back? You think they'd . . . do anything?' Since that night their mother doesn't mow the lawn in her bikini. She doesn't sleep in the nuddy with only fly-screens sealing off the house.

He snuffles. 'Nah. Just fuckin' drunk farmboys. Haven't found a gun in there though?'

'No. Spoons and shit.' Chloe kneels up, points to her trinkets. A hunk of flowered housecoat, a velvet knot that looks like a moth. A beaten tin still with the curly black cure for something stamped on its label.

'I'm the man of the house, now. Don't you reckon?'

He sucks so hard that Chloe sees a shadow scoop in his neck. 'She should of let me go out. Do something to scare them shitless. At least.'

'Bone though,' she says.

'What?'

'I got hold of a bone down there. I dropped it but . . .'

'You and that rotten lamb. You're a couple of freaks. One thing they should of done is put that fuckin' thing out its misery.' He looks away from her. 'Maybe they will next time.'

But he waits, and doesn't stop her when she lets the hair slide out of the plastic, the last tongues parting slowly, rippling quietly into the hole, a few grains lifting up to meet his smoke.

Their father had been there in the morning, gone by the time they got home from school. All the way home on the metal road that day Chloe had longed to squat and piss in the warm stones, but Michael had stopped her, angry. She tried to swerve over the grader hump, hitching her skirt in the long grass where the flies instantly prickled out, but Michael followed, dishing her a horsebite. Colour gulped to the surface of her thigh, but Chloe didn't cry. She picked up a fistful of whiter stones from the crushed tyre line, and showered them over his neck, his hair, with a swing that made her feet skid. He laughed at her rage, holding his schoolbag out as a shield. The second flash of gravel patted feebly over the canvas.

When they got home, the letter was on the kitchen bench, propped up by the toaster. The tiles had not been wiped and the letter's left edge was dusted with crumbs, a dark smudge of marmite in the corner. 'Bees make honey and flies make Marmite,' her father had always teased her. They recognised their father's writing, and Michael said they should open it. But Chloe said no, wait until Mum, you have to wait until Mum, like it says.

Michael shrugged, dumped his bag, pushed on the television. Chloe went out the back door, where she saw the fresh pen for the dying lamb. Although her father has said stay away, she straddled straight over to get to Cinders, the wire along the top of the plastic grating her cotton underpants. The juicy crease between her legs, which she didn't know the name for yet, let out a cluster of pinpricks, a pulse.

The lamb brought its face to hers, as she crouched there, piddling. The lamb's face was gummed with crusts like scrapings from the barbecue. In their city yard her father had cleaned the plate with his silver tool and Chloe had watched him pushing off those moist scabs of metal and meat. Her father hadn't been happy there. He'd wanted the farm, the farm would be different. And she could have a lamb there, he'd promised her, a lamb.

But now she knew her father was gone. She felt the contents of the letter, the gloss and slant of her father's hand, pores of dark knowledge opening, trickling. Forking in gut and throat she felt it, thick as the tattoo on the lamb's face. Her piss pumped into the grass, and Chloe thought she could hear the fly waking.

Ring, through ring, the phone keeps cutting circles in the dark house. Chloe listens to it, opening, scoring into itself like the hoops in the creek when she had watched her father throwing in a lamb packed like a milky stone.

Chloe's mother stands her in the paddock, two fencelines from the house. In the dark the buckling grass is wet, but there's no wind tonight, and Chloe feels her nightdress branching out from her body, geometric as wings.

'You know,' her mother says as she puts her down. 'Not much left now. Things worth saving.'

Chloe nods at the disc of her mother's clipped head. Its movements are still bald to her eyes. The moon makes them lonely, disjointed.

'It's hard to tell. About leaving,' her mother says. 'And about not leaving. But when you grow up, you know what. You can take. And can't take. With you.'

Her mother is shivering through each sentence. Chloe knows it's not the night but the cold of the words that keep breaking off in her.

'You know?'

Chloe nods. She thinks of her mother, holding the first letter saying he'd left them. She'd held that letter in both hands, rocking, and she'd yelled down into it as if it would answer her. Animal yells, all the words Chloe's slapped for saying. But the second letter was different, legal, the one saying that the farm was his. He wanted the money and they could stay till it sold, but that was it, witnessed. That letter her mother had just let fall onto the kitchen table. It lifted and shimmered, and she looked down into its borders as if she was staring into water, as if she could see her face pulled under its surface, in dark receding shapes.

Chloe nods again. Leaving, not leaving: she knows the difference. The sound of Michael's boots crushing the grass extends towards them now. Her mother lifts her arms, a sign of location in the dark, but also of nerves. Her hard grace. Her hands stay stretched to his chest, extracting the dark object he carries.

The exchange is complex, slow: Chloe knows it is a rite. Her mother cradles it into Chloe's arms. The lamb is made of black ribbons.

She is not surprised that the lamb is weightless, floats on her crossed wrists, ribs. Chloe has been waiting for this evolution. She knows it is the fly she's holding.

'Not much now,' her mother repeats. 'Won't take long.'

She moves away a few steps, turns. 'You two stand. Back. Clear.'

Chloe and Michael stand in the paddock. The sound of their mother threading the fence dissolves.

'What if . . .' Chloe starts to say, once.

'They'll think it's those fuckin' dumb farmboys, that's what. Ha.'

'But what about . . .'

'The animals? Fuckin' animals will be fine. They care about the animals round here.' His voice has dropped back into bullying. It is a relief to Chloe. She asks another question just to hear him spit, 'Fuck, shut up. She told you.'

They are quiet again when the first flame hollows, shifts against the sky. Their mother is right: it doesn't take long for the fire to build a cave before them, burst and strip the house. Strands and vessels of house come loose, fleck the night. They watch through the filter of the fences, red light running through the long dark lines, but they don't stand on the axis they expected. It is not the old house their mother has walked towards.

From the site of the new house Chloe sees strange things untied, in plaits and splinters. 'To move through the air by the aid of wings, the force of wind or other impulse,' she chants inside herself, from the dictionary, 'to flutter, vibrate, or play, as a flag; to throw or drive with violence; to discharge . . .' When she sees pages released from the house, she thinks they must be the cloudy leaves that covered her mother's wedding photos, sheet after rippling, wordless sheet. Her fingers remember the suck of static which fused each leaf across its photo. She pictures the image of her father, bending to sign a wide white treaty, the lens fixing his skull as the shadow of empty paper settles, melts across his face.

As they leave, Chloe thinks of the old man who used to own the farm, the rims of his heart lapsing, pickling. She thinks of him dying foggily in the front room of the old house, one claw rubbing the gin bottle, the last thing she pulls out of the hole, exhaling into the pitted jewel of its neck. She imagines him listening to the frothing grass as the horses part it, their bones sculpting their shitty pelts, the soft foam of pathogens passing over his lung. She imagines he thinks, at the last, that the ebb of their carcasses past the house sounds like the flux of the summer waters, the string of children they'd led through the panels of hard sand when the days were better.

Chloe thinks, he just needed a woman like her mother. He would have loved her mother, she thinks, and she pictures the two of them. In the image the man becomes much younger, his shirt rolled down to his waist. Chloe watches the dark skin, the spine with its humid muscles flickering, as he leads her mother along the beach where the sea draws its shattered black line.

XIII. DIALOGUE WITH DISTANCE

MY MOTHER KNOWS HOW TO pull the car under any stick or moon of shade. Pohutukawas coat the tar seal in cool, but once you've run out of the shade the car park sucks your feet down into black jelly, the hot seed-stones like teeth. The sand is the same, a fire of grains, but it's possible to tear across it, so you and your brother race, pale bones flying, taking a breath on a feathered patch of dune, a shadow of driftwood. Dropped on the way, towels, T-shirts, hats, broken plastic buckets.

The clear wash of sea, the white shells' crust, until your run slows, pushes deep. Once you reach the darker water you drop. You'll stay out here for hours, floating, oily, your body a star in the gloss. Your mother will watch from her sun-bathing half-sleep, turn and wave, a skinny luminous insect on the sand.

But today it is Christmas day and we have Nana. We can't jump out of the car until she's heaved out, tipped the seat. We're airless, melting in the back, the windows closed because any gust will spoil her 'Xmas set,' her rigid silver curls. She's wearing pantyhose, a coarse hissing brown, the black shoes, buckled and heeled. We moan at her to take them off, we'll hold up a towel or stand in front of the windows while she strips in the backseat. Her dismay is gentle but determined: how *could* a person peel off clothing in public, in a car park? (On the voyage into this country she slept fully, decently dressed, fearful shoes and brooch clipped on, waiting for a siren to call her from bunk to drowning.)

So we shuffle my grandmother down the beach, the family scaffolding her. She's unbalanced in the sand: each step is thick, prolonged, a slow consideration of bone and dress.

She carries her handbag: she will not leave it in the murky unknown of a car park where people remove clothes. Even with us gripping shoulder, elbow, she sinks.

We stand her just before the water, anxious, stiff. My brother and I splatter in deeper, dance and tease back at her. We prowl with sticky coils of weed, black nets hung with jagged juicy pods we love to burst at each other. We know our grandmother won't be angry because she has no anger in her, never raises her thin voice, acts out of incurable tenderness; I love her but I'm at the age where her passivity has begun to make me bully, to make me loud, resenting her softness, seeing in her tenderness a kind of paralysis. The sea and our laughter extend towards her; she recedes, not critical, not disapproving but lost. We've forgotten we're in our Christmas clothes, streak them with sand; our mother lets us, shoves her dark skirt in her knickers, swoops, kicks. We don't see the long strange wave until it's plunged through us. Then we struggle, turn up the beach toward Nana.

For a moment we see her, staring, bent, as the sea filters black shoes, blue dress, flesh. Then the rush dissolves beneath her, reverses; her fall is quiet, suspended. Face down in the membrane of salt, the instinct to fight does not seem to rise in her. She is rolled, grazed, before we reach her, fists in her breasts all the while clinging to the black straps of her handbag.

That summer I was a child and did not understand her. The landscape carved from ridges of sharp heat, the beach with its fusion of shine and water: how could her body not recognise this, not respond to it? How could she not long to swim, learn to take off her heavy respectable clothes? My mother, my brother and I lived out the summer with layers burnt from our skin, with shell fibres biting beneath our togs, with hard bare blackened feet, with our hair in salt-congealed strips like flax. We seemed to be day after fluid day at the beach, our sun-dreaming mother with unlooped bikini turning a deep greasy-brown, our child-bodies hanging in the sea studying the sun through the red net of eyelids. We understood the stories about Maui hauling up the land with a jawbone-hook: that was the kind of pull we felt towards it, like rope from bone to horizon. The beach was our home, but for my grandmother it was an alien dimension. Somehow she'd come across half the world, but she could not take another step.

We'd wanted to show her our Christmas; we'd cut her away from hers, taken her from the white lace cloth, the good china, the Queen's broadcast. Taken her from the sitting-room where she could at least imagine snow, coal, a river almost as solid and grey as the cobblestones. Back inside, enclosed in her housecoat, in the small domestic space she decorates with pieces of England, my grandmother is restored, her Christmas goes on with its stories of past and distance. Her fall has worried us, we no longer want to interrupt her rituals of longing. After dinner she drinks her tiny glass of sherry, wears a crinkled paper hat, foxtrots round the sitting-room humming a half remembered circuit of lullabies, war anthems, dance-hall tunes. The shock of the sea has been cleaned from her, she smells once more of plastic flowers, and she waltzes, jerkily, sings in a shivering voice, wrists hanging for a vanished partner. A dance of placelessness, dissonant, nostalgic: a woman who cannot stand upright here.

This Christmas we go to your room, my mother, my brother, myself. When we get there the nurses are washing you, balancing you between them on the bed. One has a cloth, crossing your skin with the lightest pattern and pressure of water; the other, bending, holds the angle of your body, croons softly into your face. Once again, this visit, your body has thinned toward the unthinkable: it takes our breathing a moment to adjust. But we stay, and we know we are somehow honoured to watch you. There is dignity in this, although our mother often whispers thanks that you don't know of this nakedness, a woman overdressed even at the water's edge, a woman who slept with her hair pressed under a net. Through your window a collage of light and trees falls across your hip, and the shade looks almost thicker than the residue of your own skin. Bald, blue-edged, the bowl of your hip seems to be your only solidity, all your limbs as bleached and slender as driftwood. I am reminded of the reason you crossed the ocean to live in this country: your daughter's body was carrying me, sealed, afloat within. That was a link, a belonging that with-stood any sense of alienation from your new land.

Above the nurses' ministrations your face is remote, your eyes not closed, but lowered into deep sockets, mauve, erased. This is the practice of Christmas now, this visit our own ritual of loss; I realise I've come to measure your loss through Christmases. I think back through these family days when your presence, once so vivid, festive, became fragmented, clouded, your songs becoming wordless, your sense of the season dis-jointed. You tried to copy down your recipes for the Christmas feast, rich, traditional; your handwriting was a sequence of knots. There was fall after fall, which in my memory all seem to stretch from that day at the beach: but we could not know then that the glitter of your own nerves was secretly waiting to drown you within yourself, an immersion deeper than the ocean. We would lose you slowly, stroke after stroke. You fall, in the house, in the street, resurface each time without a piece of history, a crucial fibre of memory burnt away: your address, one of our faces. Language shatters in your mouth, you try to tell us what is happening with broken words, untranslatable. Alzheimer's, the doctors tell us, dementia, a nursing home. Homelessness, we think.

Now, you don't speak at all: although sometimes your throat makes a sound that we think is a word-splinter, perhaps the fractured name of a child or a place. You don't look at us: but there are visits when your eyes seem to pull in their hoods, to focus. I think you stared into my face when I whispered to you that I was pregnant with my first child; I remember you moved to cradle the babies when I first set them against your ribs; I know, for a moment, you watched my two sons chanting *jingle bells* by your bedside last Christmas.

But I also know, as we visit this year, that we carry the mark of the Christmas two years back, when we sat around your bed, when the nursing home called us to say you couldn't last much longer. The light in the room was low, mottled, the bed within it like a raft. Your figure was unbearably small, a study in the body's brutal fragility. Chilled, wet-faced, my brother and I sat with our mother, listened to your breath. Each inhalation was terrible, tidal (I close my eyes: even now it is a lasting scar of sound). We touched you, ankle, cheekbone, skull, and muttered memories, songs, anything. We prayed; and each knew what we were praying for, although we thought *not Christmas, surely not Christmas*. But the night was without release, kept shifting the horizon.

This Christmas as we leave your room we hold our mother, elbow, waist. She is steady, resilient, but an only child, needing her grief shared. We walk down the corridor past room after room of families also murmuring carols, placing a mother's, a father's hand over a baby, over a gift or a spoon, hoping for a gesture, a slur of sound, a particle of light in the iris. (Last year when my sons were here singing their off-beat, giggling hymns, visitors came from these rooms to ask if I would bring the boys in to sing to them.) We go back to our mother's house and set the table with items from your history: dishes, the good cloth, the heavy food cooked in the white bowl you brought from England.

We don't want to go down to the beach. But the children are insistent. Their bodies are not constrained by our history, but straining forward into their own. When they get to the beach their agility is fierce, rhythmic, certain. So, on our next visit, they may trail sand from their dark feet onto your sheets, their pockets clicking with shells, their clothes rock-cut or watermarked. You might smell the shore on their hair, their hands on your temple may prickle with salt. I may even bring you a photo I take of my oldest son: his body is loose in the air, exultant, as he launches himself from a dune-ledge. His feet hook upward from the sand, his hands filter sky, his jaw hardens for a shout. It is a pose of discovery, of homing. But somehow, also, there is an inflection in his face, his frame, which recalls you dancing: your arms suspended for a distant partner.